Longman e[illegible]
practice kit

# GCSE Chemistry

*Mark McElroy*
*John Sadler*

**Series Editors**
Geoff Black and Stuart Wall

**Titles available**

| *GCSE* | *A-level* |
|---|---|
| Biology | Biology |
| Business Studies | Business Studies |
| Chemistry | British and European Modern History |
| English | Chemistry |
| French | Economics |
| German | French |
| Geography | German |
| Higher Mathematics | Geography |
| Information Systems | Mathematics |
| Mathematics | Physics |
| Physics | Psychology |
| Science | Sociology |

Addison Wesley Longman Ltd.,
Edinburgh Gate, Harlow,
CM20 2JE, England
*and Associated Companies throughout the World.*



First published 1997

ISBN 0582 31190-x

British Library Cataloguing-in-Publication Data
A catalogue record for this book is available from the British Library.

Set by 32 in 9/13pt Baskerville
Produced by Longman Singapore Publishers Pte
Printed in Singapore

# Acknowledgements

We are grateful for the work of the staff at Addison Wesley Longman, in particular Brigitte Allen and Linda Marsh for their helpful comments and suggestions.

Many of the figures in this book are based on original drawings by Emily Sadler, and we wish to record our thanks for her most valuable contribution.

We would like to thank the staff of the various examination groups for allowing us to use questions from their papers, and to the pupils at Dr Challoner's High School and their Chemistry teacher, Ann Bennett, for trying out some of the questions for us.

Finally, we must thank our wives Vivian and Alison for their continued patience, encouragement and support.

# Contents

# How to use this book

This book covers core topics which are common to all examination groups and some other topics that are very likely to be on your syllabus. The book is arranged in four parts.

## *Part I* Preparing for the examination

This section gives advice about what you should be doing before and during the examination. A revision planner is provided with this book to help you structure your revision, beginning some weeks before the examination. There is also an explanation of the different sorts of examination question you might face with tips to help you answer them successfully. The skills that the examiner is looking for are also explained. There is also a section to help you with your coursework. Do not ignore this advice – coursework is 25% of your total mark.

## *Part II* Topic areas, summaries and questions

This section has been split into seven key topic areas which have been chosen to give you essential information to make your revision easier. In each area you will find:

1. **Revision tips** Here guidance is given on revising that particular topic area together with aids to help you remember the topic.
2. **Topic outlines** These will not replace your own full notes but will give you most of the basic facts that you need and present the material in short fact form that is easier to revise. If you need more detail the *Longman Study Guide GCSE Chemistry* is a good source.
3. **Revision activities** To help make your revision active. These exercises will check your understanding of the topic.
4. **Practice questions** The examination questions at the end of each topic are designed to test your knowledge of the topic area. Some questions require knowledge that has not been specifically mentioned in the text, these have been set to test your breadth of knowledge in the topic area. Try your best! The questions have been laid out in the same style as that of most examination groups, with spaces left for you to fill in your answers.

## *Part III* Answers and grading

Here you will find answers to the practice questions. Use these to check your answers *after* you have attempted to answer the questions to your best ability. There are also student answers with examiner comments to show where common mistakes are made.

## *Part IV* Timed practice papers

A timed practice paper has been provided to test yourself under examination conditions. Do make sure that you try to answer the questions before you look up the answers in the next section. Don't give up too easily or you aren't making the best use of the questions!

*part I*

# Preparing for the examination

# Preparing for the examination

## Planning your revision

- Start revising early. Although last-minute revision works for some people it is a risky process.
- You should try and get the information into your long-term memory so that you can reproduce answers more easily on the day of the examination. Long-term memory depends on rehearsal and repetition.
- Brief, but constant review over a 21-day period will ensure that you can recall material months later.
- Avoiding last-minute revision, panic will help reduce examination anxiety and enable you to answer questions effectively.
- Try to get into the habit of studying in the same place at the same time each day.
- Following a schedule will help information become part of your knowledge-store, helping you to remember it as easily as you remember your home address! Use the Revision Planner at the back of this book.
- Always start with an easier topic and build up to a more difficult topic.
- Finish your revision session with a piece of work you understand.

A suggested revision schedule is as follows

| *Time after lesson* | *Revision time* | *Procedure* |
|---|---|---|
| Same day | 5 minutes | Review lesson notes, clarify information if necessary, and highlight key facts and concepts. |
| Day one | 10 minutes | Review notes. Briefly write out key points without reference to original; check back with original and use a different colour pen to underline any points you missed. |
| Day seven | 5 minutes | Reconstruct key points in revision format. Store in revision file. |
| Day twenty one | 30 minutes | Reproduce revision notes without reference to original scheme, compare and review. Highlight any points missed. |
| Three-month intervals until examinations. | 10–30 minutes | Study and duplicate review notes on topics. |

- Be prepared to be flexible with the above schedule. It may take you longer to revise some subjects than others.
- Make sure your revision schedule includes your other subjects.
- The better that you understand Chemistry; the more you will enjoy it. Once you start enjoying a subject it becomes much easier to learn.
- Do not just read your notes, try other activities such as:
  - Using post-it stickers to keep track of your review schedule.
  - Using colours for underlining and highlighting can help you to remember important information.
  - Much of memory is visual. Consider the layout of your notes, use space and symbols to make them easy to read and attractive to the eye.
  - Label any diagrams you draw in pencil so that you can rub them out and test yourself again later on.

- Be prepared to work hard. You should work through your notes regularly until you are certain that you understand a topic completely.
- If you do have problems with a topic ask a friend or your teacher to explain it to you. Also, do help other people who are having problems. Working together is another way that helps you (and your friend) to commit information to your long-term memory.
- Practice the questions given in this book.
- Lastly, it is the quality of your revision that counts *not* the quantity of time you spend on it

## Advice about the examination

Remember that:

- The examination question papers are written carefully by experienced teachers.
- They want you to show what you know, understand and can do – there are no trick questions. Each question is carefully looked at to make sure that it is clear and easy to understand.
- The examination boards do *not* have to fail a certain number of candidates. There are agreed standards for each grade; you will get the grade for the standard you have reached. For example, a candidate who can write symbol equations correctly is more likely to get a higher grade than a candidate who can write a word equation
- Try and get a syllabus from the examination group you are taking your examination with.
- Find out whether you are taking the Foundation level or the Higher level – the content differs for the different levels.

### *The day before the examination*

- Get ready, collect all the equipment you will need and a spare for each. Do not rely on old pen cartridges or old calculator batteries.
- Have a relaxing day and a good night's sleep.
- Don't cram – last-minute revision may confuse you.
- Double check that you have correct details of where and when the examination will take place.

### *Mathematical requirements*

At **Foundation level** you are expected to have the following mathematical knowledge and skills:

- Evaluate expressions incorporating the four operations: addition, subtraction, multiplication and division.
- Make approximations and estimates to obtain reasonable answers.
- Use simple formulae expressed in words.
- Use of tables and charts.
- Draw graphs from given data, selecting appropriate scales for the axes.
- Choose by simple inspection, and then draw, the best smooth curve through a set of points on a graph.
- Interpret graphs in terms of general trends and by interpolation.
- Read interprete and draw simple references from tables.
- Vulgar and decimal fractions and percentages.
- Solve simple equations.
- Elementary ideas and applications of common measures of rate.
- Measure averages and the purposes for which they are used.
- Substitute numbers for words and letters in formulae (without transformation of simple formulae).
- Understand that a measurement given to a whole number may be inaccurate by up to one-half in either direction.

In addition, **Higher level** candidates should be familiar with:

- Squares and square roots.
- Conversion between vulgar (such as $\frac{1}{4}$ or $\frac{3}{4}$) and decimal fractions (such as 0.25 or 0.75) and percentages (such as 25 % and 75 %).
- The four rules applied to improper fractions (such as $\frac{3}{2}$ or $\frac{7}{4}$) and mixed fractions.
- Expression of one quantity as a percentage of another, percentage change.
- Idea of gradient.
- Determine the intercept of a linear graph.
- Manipulate simple formulae, equations and expressions.
- Simple linear equations in one unknown.
- Elementary ideas and applications of direct and inverse proportion.

## Types of examination questions

- There are no multiple-choice questions in Chemistry.
- Questions are at either Foundation level or Higher level.
- A structured question consists of a number of parts (a), (b) (c) etc., and these parts might be further sub-divided into (i), (ii), (iii) etc.
- When a part of the question is sub-divided then there is a link between the parts – so that one answer leads onto the next.
- Each part requires a short answer and the mark for each section is given.
- There is a space to fill in your answer and this will give you a guide as to how much to write. Also use the mark to check how much time to spend on the question – as a general rule, one mark equals one minute; e.g. [3] will indicate that there are three marks for that section; make sure that you have written three separate points.
- Always include units with your numerical answers.
- You may need to use data to answer questions for certain examination boards, for the examination a data booklet will be supplied. We have included a data chapter at the end of this book for use with the practice questions.

### *Essay questions*

The Higher level papers may contain essay questions. These are questions that require answers that are longer than one or two sentences.

- Make a plan of your answers.
- Write neatly and legibly.
- Keep your answer concise and to the point – you can only score marks by answering the question.
- Plan your time.

### *Command words*

Look for instruction words in the question such as describe and explain. These tell you the type of answer to give. Here are some instruction words, but ask your teacher if you find any others in past papers or the syllabuses.

- **Compare/Constrast** Point out similarities and differences, advantages and disadvantages of the items mentioned in the question, e.g. compare and contrast the properties of ethane and ethene.
- **Define** Give the exact meaning of a term, principle or procedure, e.g. define the term fossil fuel.
- **Describe** Give a full account of the main points of the topic, using diagrams where appropriate. The marks for the question will indicate how much detail you should include, e.g. describe what you would observe if magnesium ribbon were added to copper sulphate solution.
- **Explain** Give the reasons for, e.g. explain how adding sodium carbonate to hard water removes the hardness.

- **List/Name** Give a number of points or facts required rather than sentences. No explanation is needed, e.g. name the gas given off when hydrogen peroxide decomposes.
- **Outline** Briefly give all the essential points, e.g. outline how you would show that chlorine was more reactive than bromine.
- **Sketch** Do a simple free-hand drawing that show correct proportions and important details, e.g. sketch the apparatus you would use to fractionally distil crude oil.
- **State** Give a brief answer, with little or no explanation, e.g. state Le Chatelier's Principle.
- **Suggest** Implies that there is no one correct answer. You should use your overall knowledge of the subject, e.g. suggest one method by which substances made of iron could be removed from waste materials.

## Assessment objectives

- These are the objective you will be tested on in the examination.
- The assessment objectives for Chemistry are:
  1. Carry out experimental and investigative work in which you plan procedures, use precise and systematic ways of making measurement and observations, analyse and evaluate evidence and relate this to chemical knowledge and understanding.
  2. Recall, understand, use and apply the knowledge of Chemistry set out in the syllabus.
  3. Communicate chemical observations, ideas and arguments using a range of scientific and technical vocabulary and appropriate scientific and mathematical conventions.
  4. Evaluate relevant chemical information and make informal judgements from it.
- The percentage of marks awarded to each of these objectives will be approximately for **1** 25% for **2** 60% and for **3** and **4** 15%.
- Objective **1** will be tested by coursework.
- Objectives **2**, **3** and **4** will be tested by a written examination at the end of your course – the GCSE examination.

## During the examination

- Arrive at the examination room early and try to relax.
- Once in the room, listen carefully to everything the invigilator says, he or she has important instructions to give you.
- If you do not understand the instructions, ask.
- Use all the time you are given to answer the question paper. You do not get extra marks by finishing early and you may lose marks by rushing.
- Pace yourself, plan your time.

### *For all the written examinations*

- Read the instructions carefully, particularly the rubric. (The rubric tells you, among other things, how many questions you should answer.)
- Make sure you write in the information requested, such as your name, candidate number, centre number and the name of the paper, on all the answer sheets you hand in.
- Calculate how much time you can spend on each question; allow time for reading the question, planning your answer, writing it and reading it over.

### *For short answer or structured written papers*

- Make sure you know how many questions you have to answer and whether the paper has sections (these details will be shown in the rubric on the front sheet of the question paper).

- Make sure you answer the compulsory questions first and the correct number of questions overall.
- Underline the key words on the question paper to help you keep to the point in your answer.
- Do not waste time by repeating the question in your answer.
- If you start to dry up on one question, leave space and move on. You are likely to gain more marks on the next question than you will by struggling on with the present one.
- If you feel your answer is incomplete, leave sufficient space below it so that you can come back to it later on thus keeping the answer all in one place.
- When answering structured questions answer *all* the different sections because each part carries a certain number of marks.
- Write down the answers the examiner has asked for, not all the things you can possibly tell the examiner on the subject, e.g. if you were asked to list three items, list three. You will not get extra marks for listing four or more.
- Help the examiners by numbering your answers clearly and correctly. Show all your working. If you make a mistake, do not rub it out, simply cross it through.
- Make your sketches and drawings a reasonable size (not too small). Label them clearly and include all essential points.
- When you draw a graph, make sure that it uses up most of the graph paper. Label the graph clearly.
- If you start to run out of time, write short, accurate notes instead of sentences.
- If you have time, read through your answers and check any calculations you have made.

## Coursework

All the examining boards will award up to three marks for spelling, punctuation and grammar for **coursework only.** The performance criteria are the same for all the boards.

- **Threshold performance (1 mark)** Candidates spell, punctuate and use the rules of grammar with reasonable accuracy; they use a limited range of specialist terms appropriately.
- **Intermediate performance (2 marks)** Candidates spell, punctuate and use the rules of grammar with considerable accuracy; they use a good range of specialist terms with facility.
- **High performance (3 marks)** Candidates spell, punctuate and use the rules of grammar with almost faultless accuracy, deploying a range of grammatical constructions; they use a wide range of specialist terms adeptly and with precision.

### *P Plan experimental procedures*

You will be expected to suggest ideas to investigate. You could carry out preliminary ideas, before making a plan on how to carry out the investigation. Decide on the observations and measurements you are going to take and decide how you will control key variables. Finally decide on the apparatus and equipment that you are going to use, but above all make sure that your experiment is safe. Your teacher will certainly help you here.

### *O Obtain evidence*

Using the apparatus and ideas in planning, you will carry out the investigation making observations and measurements with care and accuracy. Make sure that your observations are relevant and if necessary repeat observations and measurements. Record all your results in an orderly and appropriate manner.

### *A Analyse evidence and drawing conclusions*

You must present both your qualitative and quantitative work clearly using graphs if appropriate. You should look for trends or patterns in your results. Make sure that your conclusions are valid and that your numerical results have an appropriate degree of accuracy. (If you have weighed chemicals to one decimal point of accuracy, you must not give conclusions containing several decimal points!). Finally, you must decide whether your results support your initial idea when planning and you must explain any conclusions to the best of your ability.

### *E Evaluate evidence*

Once you have finished the investigation you should consider whether you collected sufficient evidence and the right evidence. You must look at the results carefully to see if there are any strange outcomes which might be rejected. Finally, you might like to make suggestions to improve the methods you have used and to suggest further ideas for investigation. (Remember you are also assessed on spelling, punctuation and grammar.)

To gain marks in your coursework you must have carried out at least **two pieces of work** to cover all **four skill areas** and at least one of the skill area marks must have been obtained from a **whole investigation**; i.e. a piece of work which covered all four skill areas. Your teacher will make sure that you have performed at least the minimum amount of two pieces of work.

## Certificates

After all your hard work, hopefully you will be awarded with a certificate. The certificate will show this subject as **SCIENCE: CHEMISTRY**. The GCSE grades are A*, A, B, C, D, E, F and G. The highest grade is A* and the lowest grade is G. If you do not pass you are ungraded. Make sure that you do not fall into that category.

### And finally

Remember that doing your best is not about luck. Success in examinations is based on sound knowledge, practised skills and thorough preparation.

*part II*

# Topic areas, summaries and questions

# 1 States of matter, elements, mixtures and compounds

## REVISION TIPS

- Draw the arrangement of particles (small spheres) in each of the three states of matter. Beneath each arrangement describe the position and motion of the particles incorporating the key words: **orderly**, **random**, **vibrate**, **move around**, **close-packed** and **far apart**.
- Make a list of simple explanations for the following processes:
  - Brownian motion
  - compression(in gases)
  - diffusion
  - evaporation
  - expansion
  - melting and boiling
  - sublimation (NICCEA only).
- Avoid common errors by noting the following:
  - In changes of state such as melting and boiling, **particles do not break down**.
  - In expansion and contraction the particles of matter **do not change their size**. It is the space between them that changes.

***Elements, compounds and mixtures***

- Learn the definitions of an element and a compound with some examples of each.
- The differences between mixtures and compounds can be remembered by **SPEC**: **S**eparated; **P**roperties; **E**nergy and **C**omposition
- Draw simple line diagrams of the apparatus commonly used to separate mixtures into their component parts.

## TOPIC OUTLINE

### Key definitions

- **Solids** have definite volumes and shapes. They cannot be compressed. They are usually the densest of the three states.
- **Liquids** have definite volumes but take the shape of their container. They cannot be compressed.
- **Gases** take the shape of their container, but can be compressed. They escape from open containers by diffusion.
- **Diffusion** is the process by which gases and liquids *mix without being stirred or shaken*.
- **An element** is a substance that cannot be split up or separated into anything simpler.
- **A compound** is a substance formed by a chemical reaction between two or more elements.
- **A mixture** consists of two or more components (elements or compounds) not chemically combined together.

## States of matter

- The particles in a **solid** are close-packed and vibrating.
- The particles in a **liquid** are slightly further apart than in a solid and have free random motion.
- The particles in a **gas** are about 10 times further apart than in liquids and have free, random motion.

Typical sample diagrams used in exams:

*Figure 1.1*

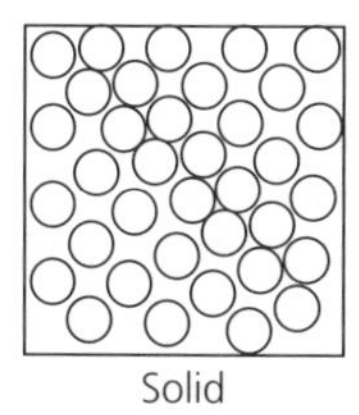
Solid

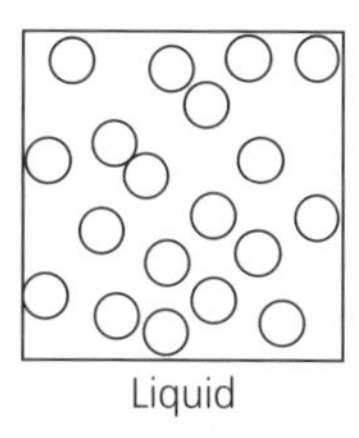
Liquid

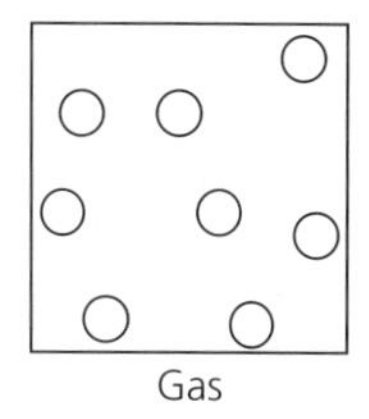
Gas

- A **change of state** of matter can be achieved by the addition or removal of energy at the melting or boiling point.

KEY POINT

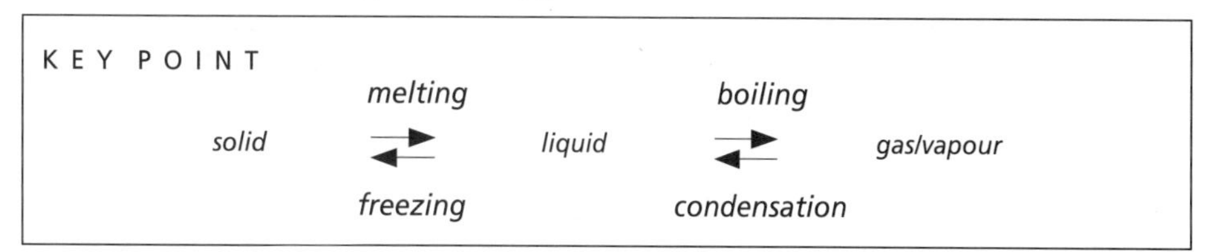


- **Melting** occurs when energy is absorbed by particles in the solid state at the melting point. This frees the particles from the orderly arrangement of the solid lattice, causing them to move about freely.
- **Boiling** occurs when energy is absorbed by particles in the liquid state at the boiling point. This allows the particles to move much further apart , and even more freely in the vapour state.

HINT
*There is no temperature rise in either of these changes of state.*

- **Evaporation** can occur at temperatures below the boiling point. The particles in the liquid state take in heat energy and enter the vapour state. Therefore, evaporation without added heat causes cooling of the remaining liquid. Examples of this effect include perspiration cooling and the application of cooling sprays to dull the pain of muscular injury in sport.
- **Expansion** occurs in all three states as the addition of more energy causes the *particles* to get further apart. The particles themselves do not change size! **Contraction** is the opposite of expansion.
- **Diffusion** in gases occurs because the particles are in continuous random motion and are far enough apart for intermixing to occur. Diffusion in solids does not occur because the particles are too closely packed to allow intermixing.
- **Brownian motion** occurs when microscopic particles of solid or liquid are bombarded by the invisible molecules of the surrounding gas or liquid. Through the microscope it appears that the particles are being jostled by invisible forces.

HINT
*Brownian motion occurs in smoke – where the smoke particles are bombarded by air molecules; and in milk – where the fat droplets are bombarded by water molecules.*

## The Gas Laws

- The **temperature** of a substance in degrees Kelvin (absolute temperature) is related to the kinetic energy of its molecules.
- **Pressure** in gases is produced by the bombardment of the sides of the container by gas molecules. The faster the molecules move (higher temperature) the higher the **collision rate** and the greater the pressure.
- The **volume** of a gas increases as its temperature rises. Increased temperature causes molecules to move faster. This increases the number of collisions with other molecules leading to more space between them and so a greater volume.

KEY POINT
$P \propto T$ *and* $V \propto T$ *(in degrees K). So* $P \times V \propto T$ **for a fixed mass of gas.**
*This gives* $\frac{P \times V}{T}$ = **constant.**

*Example*
The volume of a gas is 2 litres at 298 K and 1 atmosphere pressure. What is its volume at the same temperature and a pressure of 4 atmospheres?

$\frac{P_1V_1}{T_1} = \frac{P_2V_2}{T_2}$ for a fixed mass of gas.

Substituting, we get $\frac{1 \times 2}{298} = \frac{4 \times V_2}{298}$ from which $V_2$ is 0.5 litre($dm^3$)

## Elements, compounds and mixtures

HINT
*Gases – particles far apart; liquids – particles almost touching; solids – orderly arrangement.*

- The diagrams below show a gaseous element, a liquid compound and a solid mixture.

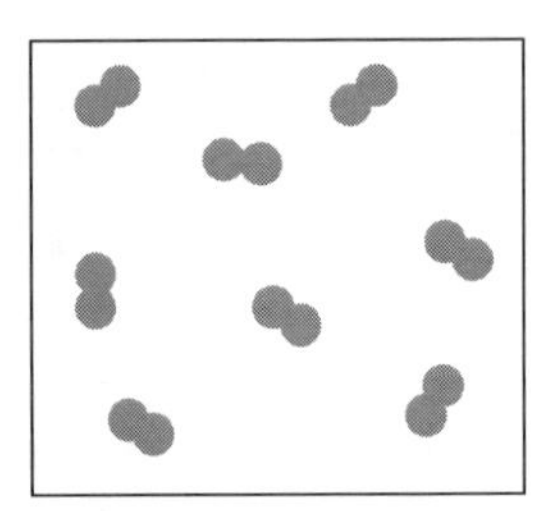

*Figure 1.2*
A gaseous element

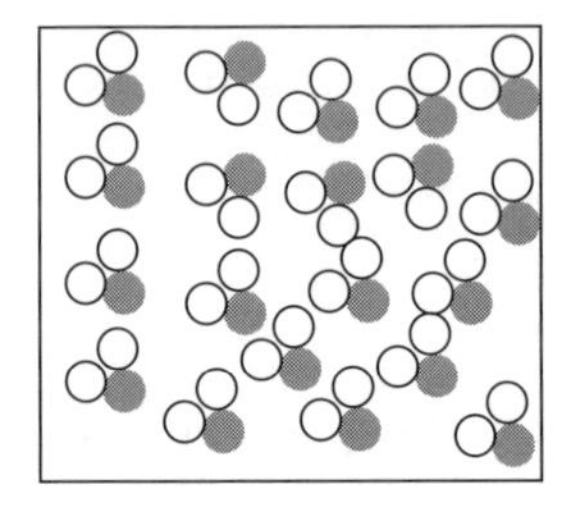

*Figure 1.3*
A liquid compound

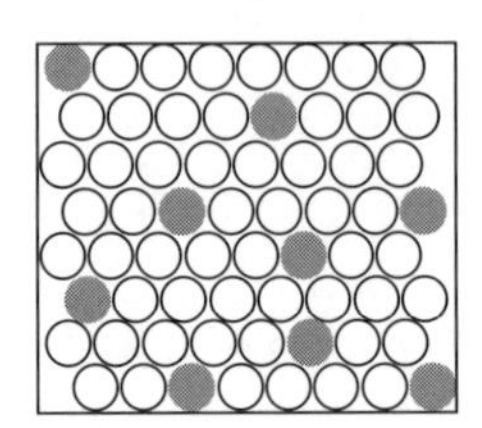

*Figure 1.4*
A solid mixture

- **Examples** of mixtures include: all solutions; soil; most rocks, e.g. granite; beverages, e.g. colas and tea; air; sea and pond – waters; rock salt.
- Their **uses** are mostly obvious but, some that are not are given below.
  - Sea water (brine) or dissolved rock salt produce chlorine and sodium hydroxide when electrolysed.
  - Granite is a building stone.

### *Separation methods*

HINT
*In mixtures of gases the separate components of the mixture cannot be seen.*

Methods of separating mixtures into their components are important because pure substances are needed for industrial processes.

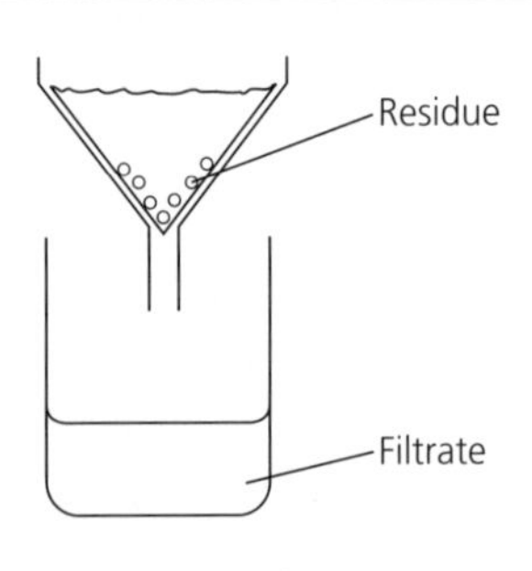


*Figure 1.5* Filtration

- **Filtration** separates a solid from a liquid using a filter paper supported in a funnel (Fig. 1.5).
- **Decanting** also separates a solid from a liquid. In decanting, the mixture is left to settle. The liquid is then carefully poured off the solid.
- A **centrifuge** separates a solid and a liquid by spinning a tube containing the mixture in a circle at several thousand revolutions per minute. The solid is forced to the bottom of the tube allowing the liquid to be decanted easily.
- **Fractional distillation** separates mixtures of liquids (**fractions**) into their components (Fig. 1.6). Boiling the mixture causes the components to vaporise in succession – the liquid with the lowest boiling point vaporising first. The vapours are condensed in a water-cooled (Liebig) condenser and collected separately as **distillates**. For example, wine on distillation will produce two distillates – ethanol (alcohol) and water, in that order.
- **Simple distillation** is similar to fractional distillation. The process involves the evaporation of a liquid from a mixture of a liquid and a solid followed by condensation of the vapour (Fig. 1.7). The condensed liquid is called the distillate. For example sea water on distillation will produce pure water as the distillate and sea salts as a **residue**.

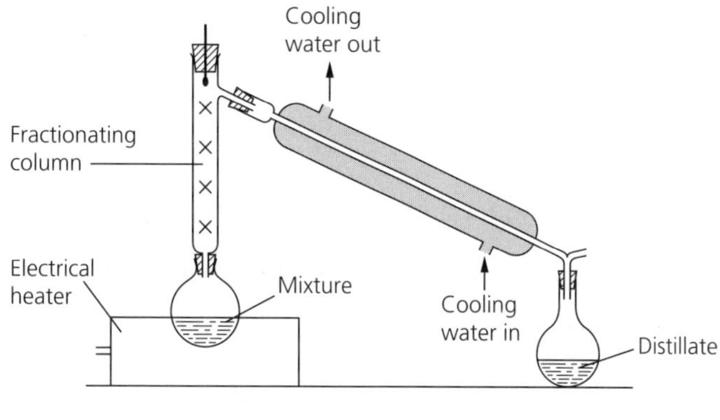


*Figure 1.6*
Fractional distillation

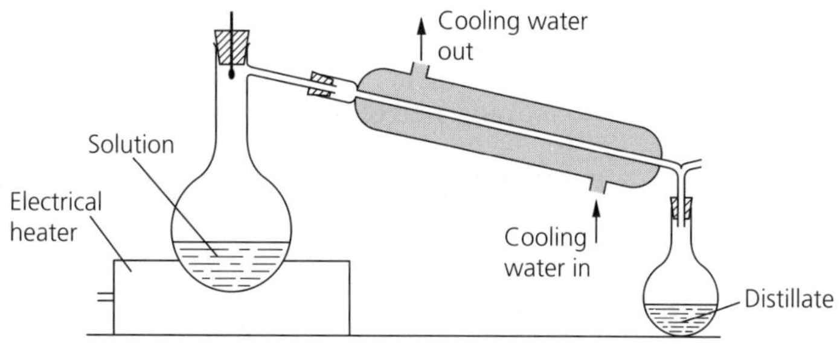


*Figure 1.7*
Simple distillation

- **Crystallisation** occurs when a **hot, saturated** solution is allowed to cool. The crystals that form will be the pure solid component if solvent is the only other component. Decanting the remaining solution allows the crystals to be dried on a tissue and so obtained pure.
- **Paper chromatography** is the process of separating a mixture of solids, in s solution, on a sheet of paper. The process is shown in Figure 1.8 for a mixture of two solids A and B. Careful examination of the diagram will show how the process is carried out. The main points are:
  - A horizontal pencil line with a spot of the mixture on it.
  - Running solvent level below the pencil line.
  - Vessel covered to prevent solvent evaporation

HINT
*Remember that even colourless mixtures can be separated by chromatography – but the spots must be exposed with ultraviolet (u.v.) light or a special chemical treatment.*

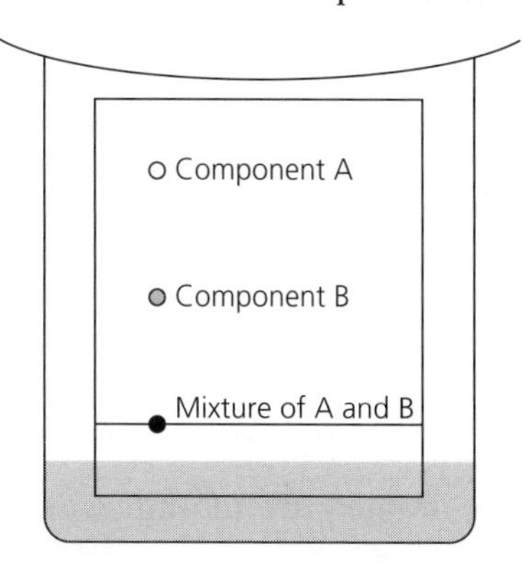


*Figure 1.8*
Chromatography

## REVISION ACTIVITIES

**1** . . . . . . . . . . . . . . . . . cannot be compressed because their particles are as closely packed as possible. Gases are compressible because their particles are . . . . . . . . . . . . . . . . .  . . . . . . . . . . . . . . . . . and increasing the pressure pushes them closer together.

**2** When a solid is heated at its . . . . . . . . . . . . . . . . . . . . . . . . . . . . . . . . . . its temperature does not change until melting is complete. The energy gained by the solid as it melts causes its particles to . . . . . . . . . . . . . . . . . . . . . . . . . . . . . . . . . . more freely.

3 . . . . . . . . . . . . . . . . is the name of the process by which liquids or gases mix.

4 Perspiration causes cooling because the evaporation of moisture requires

. . . . . . . . . . . . . . . . . . . . . . . . . . . . . . . . . which is taken from the body.

5 Sea water and wine are both mixtures because when they are distilled they

. . . . . . . . . . . . . . . . . into at least . . . . . . . . . . . . . . . . . components.

6 State one method commonly used to carry out the following processes:

(a) Getting clear water from muddy water – . . . . . . . . . . . . . . . . . . . . . . . . . .

(b) Identifying the dyes used to colour an ink – . . . . . . . . . . . . . . . . . . . . . . . .

(c) Obtaining petrol from crude oil – . . . . . . . . . . . . . . . . . . . . . . . . . . . . . . .

(d) Getting table sugar from the watery extract of sugar cane or beet –

. . . . . . . . . . . . . . . . . . . . . . . . . . . . . . . . . . . . . . . . . . . . . . . . . . . . . .

7 Give one common use for each of the following.

The element : copper . . . . . . . . . . . . . . . . . .

The compound : sulphuric acid . . . . . . . . . . . . . . . . . .

The mixture: brine . . . . . . . . . . . . . . . . . .

## PRACTICE QUESTIONS

***Question 1 – Foundation***

(a) Give the name and symbol of an element.

Name . . . . . . . . . . . . . . . . . . . . . . . Symbol . . . . . . . . . . . . . . . . . . . . . . . [2]

(b) Give the name and formula of a compound.

Name . . . . . . . . . . . . . . . . . . . . . . . Formula . . . . . . . . . . . . . . . . . . . . . . [2]

(c) (i) Give the name of a mixture in everyday use. . . . . . . . . . . . . . . . . . . . . . . . [1]

(ii) Give a use for the mixture you have chosen. . . . . . . . . . . . . . . . . . . . . . . [1]

(iii) Give the name of one pure substance in the mixture you have chosen.

. . . . . . . . . . . . . . . . . . . . . . . . . . . . . . . . . . . . . . . . . . . . . . . . . . [1]

(d) The diagrams below show the particles of an element, a compound and a mixture. Label each diagram 'element', 'mixture' or 'compound'. [2]

● and ○ represent atoms of different elements

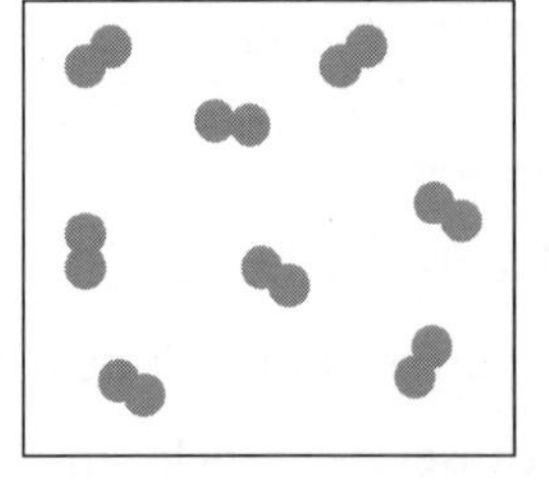

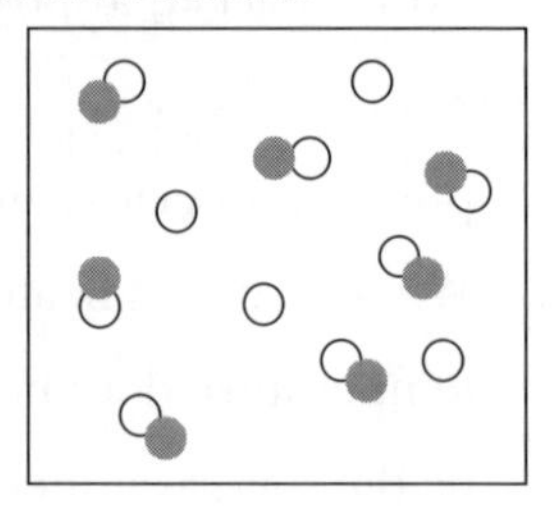

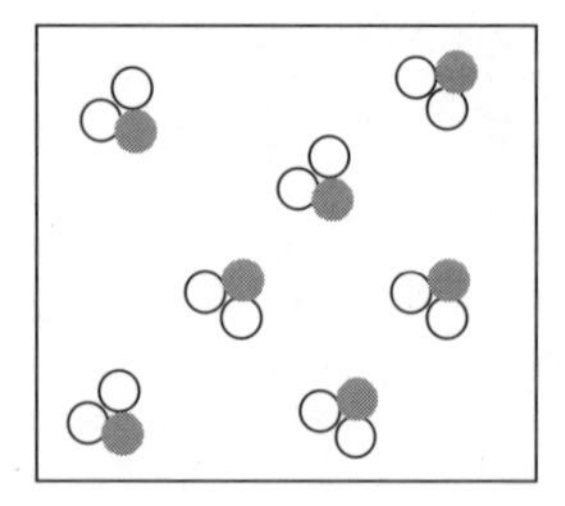

*Figure 1.9*

. . . . . . . . . . . . . . . . . . . . . . . . . . . . . . . . . . . . . . . . . . . . . . . . . . . . . . . .

(e) In the diagrams, the element, compound and mixture are all shown in the same physical state (solid, liquid or gas). Give the state and explain how you arrive at your answer. ..................................................

.............................................................

............................................................. [2]

**Total: 11 marks**
(London)

***Question 2 – Foundation***

(a) The diagram shows a burning candle.
Write beside each letter **A**, **B** and **C** to show if the candle wax in that part is *solid*, *liquid* or *gas*. Write on the diagram. [3]

A..........................................

B..........................................

C..........................................

*Figure 1.10*

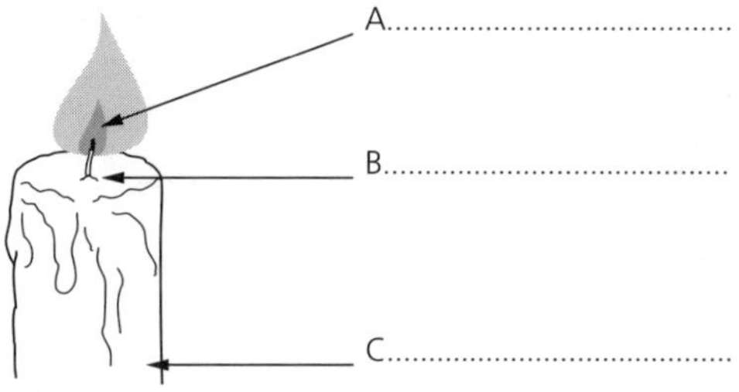

(b) (i) The first box below shows the particles in a solid metal. Complete the other boxes to show the particles when the metal is a liquid and when it is a gas. [2]

Solid Liquid Gas

Particle

*Figure 1.11*

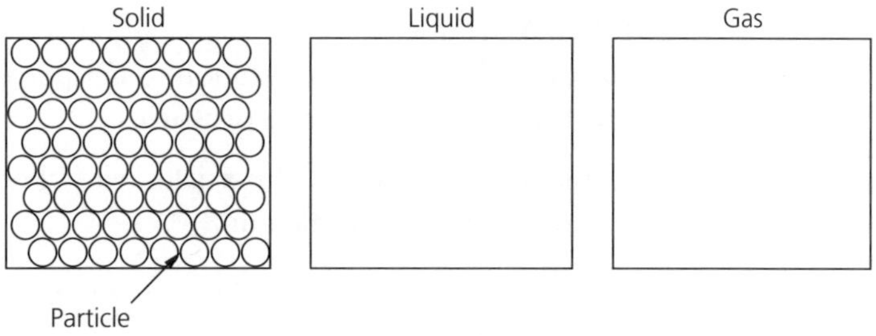

(ii) When the solid is heated it expands. Explain what happens to the particles as the solid metal expands. ..........................................

.............................................................

.............................................................

............................................................. [3]

**Total: 8 marks**
(SEG)

***Question 3 – Foundation***

Use words from the list below to fill in the spaces.

**gas** **liquid** **solid**

(a) A ............. takes the shape of the container into which it is poured. [1]

(b) When placed in a syringe a .................. can be squeezed so that it takes up much less space. [1]

(c) A .................. has a definite shape. [1]

(d) When released into a room a .................. will spread out to fill the whole room. [1]

**Total: 4 marks**
(NEAB)

***Question 4 – Higher***

Rock salt contains insoluble solids and soluble salt, sodium chloride. The following processes are needed to separate sodium chloride from rock salt.

| Addition of water | Crystallisation | Evaporation | Filtration | Stirring |
|---|---|---|---|---|

Put each process in the correct order. Explain the purpose of each process.

First process: . . . . . . . . . . . . . . . . . . . . . . . . . . . . . . . . . . . . . . . . . . . .

Purpose: . . . . . . . . . . . . . . . . . . . . . . . . . . . . . . . . . . . . . . . . . . . . . . .

Second process: . . . . . . . . . . . . . . . . . . . . . . . . . . . . . . . . . . . . . . . . . .

Purpose: . . . . . . . . . . . . . . . . . . . . . . . . . . . . . . . . . . . . . . . . . . . . . . .

Third process: . . . . . . . . . . . . . . . . . . . . . . . . . . . . . . . . . . . . . . . . . . . .

Purpose: . . . . . . . . . . . . . . . . . . . . . . . . . . . . . . . . . . . . . . . . . . . . . . .

Fourth process: . . . . . . . . . . . . . . . . . . . . . . . . . . . . . . . . . . . . . . . . . . .

Purpose: . . . . . . . . . . . . . . . . . . . . . . . . . . . . . . . . . . . . . . . . . . . . . . .

Fifth process: . . . . . . . . . . . . . . . . . . . . . . . . . . . . . . . . . . . . . . . . . . . .

Purpose: . . . . . . . . . . . . . . . . . . . . . . . . . . . . . . . . . . . . . . . . . . . . . . .

[1 mark for each process plus its purpose] **Total: 5 marks**
(SEG)

***Question 5 – Higher***

NOTE
*This question has a student answer with examiner's comments on p. 89.*

A motorist called at a filling station to get petrol, to check the oil level in the engine and to check the tyre pressures.

(a) (i) Explain fully, in terms of particles, why the motorist could smell petrol as it was being put into the tank.

. . . . . . . . . . . . . . . . . . . . . . . . . . . . . . . . . . . . . . . . . . . . . . . . . . .

. . . . . . . . . . . . . . . . . . . . . . . . . . . . . . . . . . . . . . . . . . . . . . . . . . . [3]

(ii) Explain why the smell is more noticeable on a warm summer's day than during winter.

. . . . . . . . . . . . . . . . . . . . . . . . . . . . . . . . . . . . . . . . . . . . . . . . . . .

. . . . . . . . . . . . . . . . . . . . . . . . . . . . . . . . . . . . . . . . . . . . . . . . . . . [2]

(b) After filling up with petrol, the motorist checked the oil level. Some oil was needed but as it was being added some was spilled on the ground. Explain, in terms of particles/kinetic theory, why it would take much longer for the oil spill to disappear than a petrol spill.

. . . . . . . . . . . . . . . . . . . . . . . . . . . . . . . . . . . . . . . . . . . . . . . . . . .

. . . . . . . . . . . . . . . . . . . . . . . . . . . . . . . . . . . . . . . . . . . . . . . . . . . [3]

(c) The motorist then checked the tyre pressures. The car was then driven along a motorway to the next town. On checking the tyres again it was found that the pressure in each tyre had changed. Explain fully why the pressure had changed.

. . . . . . . . . . . . . . . . . . . . . . . . . . . . . . . . . . . . . . . . . . . . . . . . . . .

. . . . . . . . . . . . . . . . . . . . . . . . . . . . . . . . . . . . . . . . . . . . . . . . . . . [4]

**Total: 12 marks**
(NICCEA)

# 2 Atomic structure, bonding and the Periodic Table

## REVISION TIPS

- Make a table of the particles in the atom. Put in the detail of their relative masses and charges. **PEN** (**P**rotons, **E**lectrons, **N**eutrons) will help you to remember the particles.
- Draw dot or cross diagrams of the electron arrangements of the first 20 elements together with the shortened forms of their electron arrangements for ease of revision, for example

| *Element* | *Electron arrangement* | *Element* | *Electron arrangement* |
|---|---|---|---|
| H | 1 | He | 2 |
| Li | 2, 1 | Be | 2, 2 etc. |

- Learn to use your Periodic Table to find out the following information about elements or their atoms.
  –Atomic (proton) number of an element.
  –Number of electron shells in an atom.
  –Number of outer-shell electrons in an atom.
  –Mass number of an atom.
- Learn the names and symbols of the first three elements in Groups I, II (if necessary), VII and Group 0.
- It is a common error to show ionic bonding where covalent bonding is required and vice versa. This can be avoided by:
  –Learning that metallic elements form compounds by **transferring** their outer electrons to the outer shell of non-metallic atoms.
  –Learning that when two non-metallic elements react they form compounds by **sharing electrons**.
- Make lists of the properties and uses of the elements and their important compounds for the groups your syllabus requires you to study.

## TOPIC OUTLINE

HINT
*Remember that all matter – solid, liquid and gases – is composed of particles. These particles may be **atoms, molecules** or **ions**.*

### Key definitions

- **Atoms** are particles of matter consisting of a nucleus surrounded by one or more shells of electrons. They are the smallest particles of an element that still retain the properties of that element.
- **Molecules** are particles composed of two or more atoms bonded together, e.g. $H_2$ and $H_2O$. They are the smallest particles of elements or compounds that retain the properties of the element or compound.

HINT
*The nucleus of a hydrogen atom contains a single proton only.*

- A **nucleus** is a very small body providing nearly all the mass of the atom. It contains protons and neutrons.
- **Protons** are particles having a relative mass of one and a *single positive charge.*
- **Neutrons** are particles having the same mass as protons but *no charge.*
- **Atomic (proton) number** is the number of protons in the nucleus of an atom. Atoms of different elements have different atomic numbers. Elements are arranged in ascending atomic number order in the **Periodic Table**.

HINT
*A mass number relates to the mass of an isotope of an element, e.g. chlorine has two isotopes with mass numbers of 35 and 37.*

- **Mass number** is the number of protons *plus* neutrons in the nucleus of an atom.
- **Electrons** are particles having a *single negative charge* which occupy **shells** around the nucleus of an atom. The number of electrons in a neutral atom equals the number of protons in its nucleus, i.e. the atomic number.
- **Isotopes** are atoms of the same element having different mass numbers. For example, chlorine has two isotopes called **chlorine-35** and **chlorine-37**. Both have an atomic (proton) number of 17 but have 18 and 20 neutrons, respectively. About 75% of all chlorine atoms are Cl-35 atoms.

*Example*
Boron, atomic number 5, has two isotopes, **B-10** and **B-11**, with mass numbers of 10 and 11 respectively. Calculate the number of protons and neutrons in each isotope.

Mass number = proton number + neutron number

Because they are isotopes, they are atoms of the same element and so have the same proton number: 5.

**B-10** has 5 protons *plus* 5 neutrons to give a mass number of 10.

**B-11** has 5 protons *plus* 6 neutrons to give a mass number of 11.

## Atomic structure

HINT
*Where more than one atom is present in a diagram, electrons in different atoms should be shown by **dots and crosses**.*

- The electrons in atoms are arranged in **shells** or **energy levels** outwards from the central nucleus, as shown in the diagram of a carbon atom (element of atomic number, 6) below.

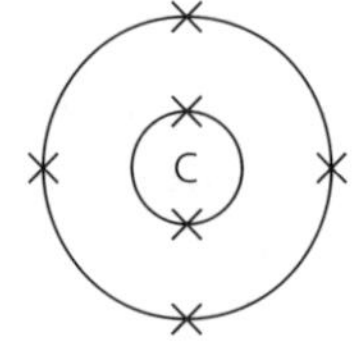


*Figure 2.1*
Electron shells in a carbon atom

HINT
*The shorthand system for electron structures shows, for example, carbon as **C 2, 4** and chlorine as **Cl 2, 8, 7**.*

- As we move outwards from the nucleus, the shells can hold more electrons. The maximum number of electrons in each shell are:
  - First shell 2
  - Second shell 8
  - Third shell 8 (up to element 20: beyond that the shell may contain up to 18 electrons)
- The **outer electrons** of atoms are the ones that take part in chemical reactions. Therefore, in considering **bonding** we often show only the outer-shell electrons.

## Bonding

Atoms combine to produce new substances by either **electron transfer** or **electron sharing**.

### *Electron transfer*

This produces ions with **ionic** bonding. All the outer-shell electron(s) from the metal atom are transferred to the non-metal atom(s).

The **rules** are:

1. The number of electrons **lost** from each metal atom equals the number of electrons in the outer shell of the atom, e.g. one electron for Group I, two for Group II and three for Group III metals.
2. The number of electrons **gained** by each non-metal atom equals the number required to make the outer shell into an octet (eight electrons, a full shell), e.g. Two electrons for Group VI elements and one electron for Group VII elements.

*Example – lithium fluoride*

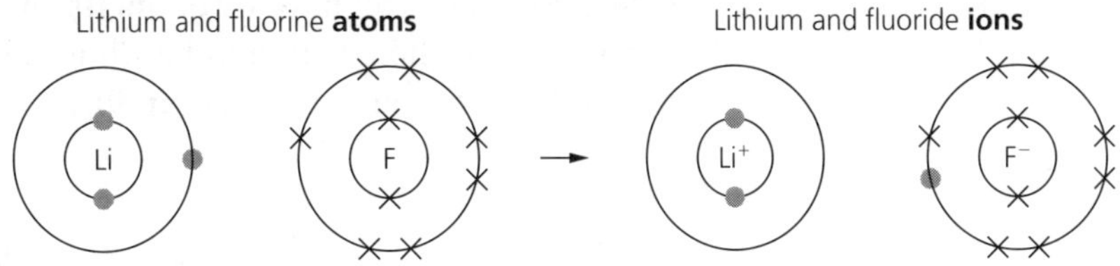

Lithium and fluorine **atoms** Lithium and fluoride **ions**

Li F → $Li^+$ $F^-$

*Figure 2.2*

H : H

*Figure 2.3* Electrons in $H_2$

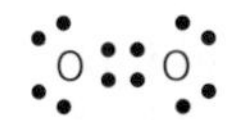

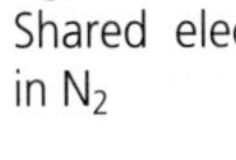

*Figure 2.4* Electrons in $O_2$

*Figure 2.5* Shared electrons in $N_2$

### *Electron sharing*

This produces molecules with **covalent** bonding. Electrons are shared in **pairs**. Each pair of shared electrons is one bond.

The rules here are:

1. The atoms contribute *equally* to the bond formed.
2. A **single bond** forms when *one electron* is contributed from *each* atom as in hydrogen, $H_2$, see Figure 2.3.
3. A **double bond** forms when *two electrons* are contributed by *each* atom as in Figure 2.4 which shows the shared electrons in oxygen, $O_2$.
4. A **triple bond** forms when *three electrons* are contributed by *each* atom as in Figure 2.5 which shows the shared electrons in nitrogen, $N_2$.

*Example – Hydrogen chloride*

When hydrogen and chlorine combine, they form a covalently bonded hydrogen chloride molecule. See below.

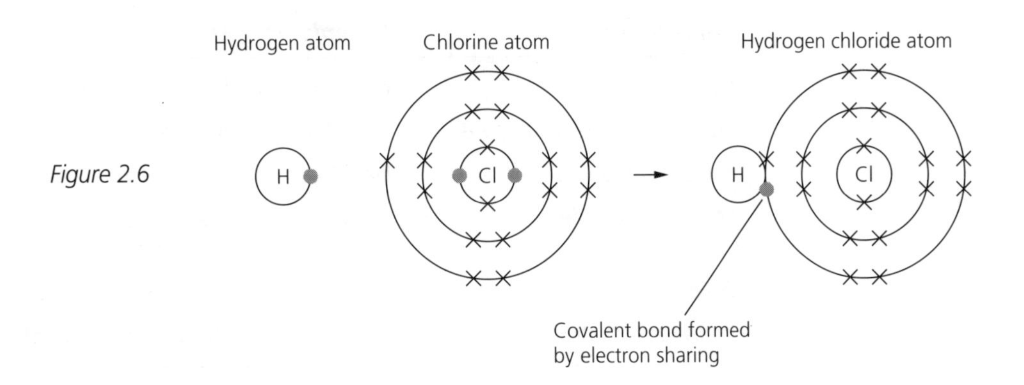


*Figure 2.6*

## The Periodic Table

> KEY POINT
> *Dobereiner and Newlands contributed to early attempts to classify elements in the years before Mendeleev made his discovery of the Periodic Table.*

- The Periodic Table, originally devised by Mendeleev, displays all the elements arranged in order of ascending atomic (proton) number.
- Elements in the Periodic Table are arranged in vertical columns (**groups**) and in horizontal rows (**periods**).
- Elements in the same group have:
  - The 'group number' of electrons in the outer shell of each atom.
  - Similar chemical and physical properties.
  - Properties which change gradually from top to bottom of the group – called a **trend**.
- Elements in the same period have:
  - The number of electron **shells** equal to the period number in their atoms.
  - The number of **outer-shell electrons** increasing in group-number order from 1 to 8 (Group 0) across the period.

    For example, elements of the **third period** have the electron structures shown below. They all have **three shells**, and the number of **outer-shell electrons** equals the group number (but there are eight outer-shell electrons for the elements in **Group 0**).

| ***Groups*** | I | II | III | IV | V | VI | VII | 0 |
|---|---|---|---|---|---|---|---|---|
| ***Period 3*** | Na | Mg | Al | Si | P | S | Cl | Ar |
| ***Electron arrangement*** | 2,8,1 | 2,8,2 | 2,8,3 | 2,8,4 | 2,8,5 | 2,8,6 | 2,8,7 | 2,8,8 |

### *Group I elements – the alkali metals*

- The elements of Group I are all soft (low melting points), grey, electrically conducting metals.
- They react vigorously with water giving off hydrogen gas and forming the corresponding **alkaline** solution of the metal hydroxide according to the equation:

  $$2M(s) + 2\ H_2O(l) \rightarrow 2\ MOH(aq) + H_2(g)$$

  Where M may be replaced by the symbol of the element – Li, Na, K, Rb or Cs.
- They are hardest, least dense and least reactive at the *top* of the group and softest, densest and the most reactive at the *bottom* of the group.
- The metals are too reactive to have many uses but sodium is used as a coolant in nuclear power plants. On the other hand the compounds of alkali metals are in common use.

| ***Name of compound*** | ***Formula*** | ***Use*** |
|---|---|---|
| Sodium chloride | NaCl | Flavouring food, de-icing roads |
| Sodium hydrogencarbonate | $NaHCO_3$ | Raising agent in foods, antacid |
| Sodium carbonate | $Na_2CO_3$ | Glassmaking, chemical manufacture |
| Sodium hydroxide | NaOH | Cleaning blocked drains; general alkali in industry |
| Potassium chloride | KCl | Salt substitute, potash fertiliser |
| Potassium nitrate | $KNO_3$ | Oxidiser in gunpowder |

***Group II elements – the alkaline earth metals***

These elements show the same trends as Group I elements.

- They are fairly soft, grey, electrically conducting metals.
- They are reactive to water, but less vigorously than Group I metals:

$$\mathbf{M}(s) + 2H_2O(l) \rightarrow \mathbf{M}(OH)_2(aq) + H_2(g)$$

where **M** may be replaced by the symbol of the Group II elements – Mg, Ca and Ba.

- They are harder than Group I metals but become softer and denser down the group.
- The metals are too reactive to have many uses but their compounds are in common use.

| *Name of compound* | *Formula* | *Use* |
|---|---|---|
| Calcium carbonate | $CaCO_3$ | Used in indigestion tablets |
| Calcium sulphate | $CaSO_4 \cdot \frac{1}{2}H_2O$ | Plaster of Paris - a medical plaster for broken limbs |
| Magnesium sulphate | $MgSO_4 \cdot 7H_2O$ | Epsom salts – a laxative in 'Health Salts' |
| Barium sulphate | $BaSO_4$ | A 'barium meal' in diagnosis of stomach ulcers |

***Group VII – the halogens***

- The halogens are all coloured – fluorine (yellow gas ); chlorine (green gas); bromine (red-brown liquid); iodine (grey solid, violet gas).
- They vary in physical state at room temperature from gases (fluorine and chlorine) through liquid (bromine) to solid (iodine), i.e. the melting and boiling points *rise* from the top to the bottom of the group – the opposite of the trend among groups of metals.
- They become denser down the group – as *all* elements do.
- They decrease in reactivity from the top to the bottom of the group – the opposite is true for metals.
- The more reactive halogens **displace** the less reactive ones from solutions of their salts. For example **chlorine** will displace bromine from solutions of bromides and iodine from solutions of iodides.

$$2NaI(aq) + Cl_2(aq) \rightarrow 2NaCl(aq) + I_2(aq)$$

$$2NaBr(aq) + Cl_2(aq) \rightarrow 2NaCl(aq) + Br_2(aq)$$

KEY POINT

*Fluorine displaces* all *the other halogens from their salt solutions. Iodine cannot displace any of the other halogens.*

| *Name of substance* | *Formula* | *Use* |
|---|---|---|
| Chlorine | $Cl_2$ | Sterilising agent for tap and swimming bath water |
| Bromine | $Br_2$ | Making anti-knock for leaded petrol |
| Iodine | $I_2$ | Antiseptic in alcohol solution |
| Sodium fluoride | NaF | Toothpaste additive |
| Sodium hypochlorite | NaOCl | Domestic bleach – 5% solution |
| Potassium iodide | KI | Additive in 'iodised salt' |
| Silver bromide/silver iodide | AgBr/AgI | Light-sensitive chemicals in photographic film |

### *Group 0 – the noble gases*

- The elements are **very unreactive**. The first three in the group form no known compounds.
- They become denser down the group and their melting points and boiling points increase.

HINT
*The uses of the noble gases depend mainly upon their unreactive nature.*

| *Name of element* | *Formula* | *Use* |
|---|---|---|
| Helium | He | Lighter-than-air ships: with oxygen in deep sea diver's 'air' supply |
| Neon | Ne | Red strip-lights and signs |
| Argon | Ar | Inert atmospheres, argon arc-welding, tungsten lamps |
| Krypton and xenon | Kr and Xe | High-intensity lamp filling |

### *Transition elements*

- Transition elements are a block of dense, metallic elements.
- They have similar properties. For instance, they all have high melting and boiling points, high densities and are much less reactive than other metallic elements.
- They form coloured compounds.
- Together with some of their compounds, they show catalytic activity.
- They are not very reactive to water (iron is an exception).
- They react with acids.

| *Name of element* | *Formula* | *Use* |
|---|---|---|
| Titanium | Ti | Aircraft, spacecraft and submarine parts |
| Chromium and nickel | Cr and Ni | Decorative and protective plating |
| Iron | Fe | Steel manufacture |
| Copper | Cu | Electrical wiring, water pipes, coinage and brass manufacture |

## REVISION ACTIVITIES

**1** The electron structure of the lithium atom can be shown as 2,1. The electron structures of the sodium atom is . . . . . . . . . . . . . . . . . and of the . . . . . . . . . . . . . . . . . atom is 2,8,8,1.

**2** (a) Identify the two types of bonds in the molecule shown in Figure 2.7. The molecule contains

(i) **single bonds** between the . . . . . . . . . . . and the . . . . . . . . . . . atoms;

(ii) a . . . . . . . . . . . . . . . . . bond between the carbon and the oxygen atom.

(b) Explain your answer.
The explanation is:

(i) . . . . . . . . . . . . . . . . . **shared electrons** make a single bond.

(ii) . . . . . . . . . . . . . . . . . . . . . . . . . . . . . . . . . . . . . . . . . . . . . . . . . . .

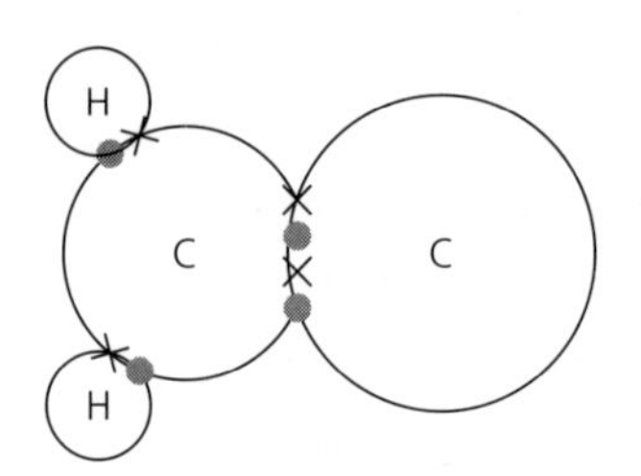


*Figure 2.7*

**3** (a) Complete the dot and cross diagram of an oxygen molecule, $O_2$.

Figure 2.8

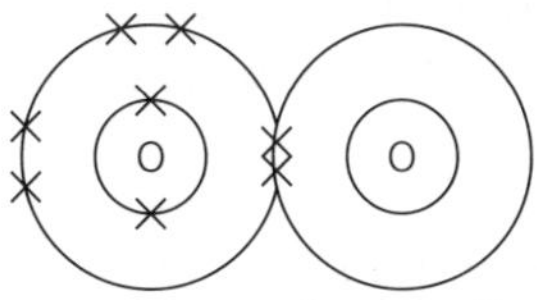

(b) Draw dot and cross diagrams to represent the formation of magnesium oxide, MgO. All electrons should be shown.

HINT
*You need to look up the atomic numbers of oxygen and magnesium to work out their electron structures.*

**4** Elements are arranged in ascending order of their . . . . . . . . . . . . . . . . . . . . . . . . . . . . . . . . . . in the . . . . . . . . . . . . . . . . . table.

**5** Rows of elements are called . . . . . . . . . . . . . . . . .

**6** Elements in the same group have the same number of . . . . . . . . . . . . . . . . . in their outer shells, but have different numbers of shells.

**7** Metallic elements are found on the . . . . . . . . . . . . . . . . .-hand side of the Periodic Table whereas non-metallic elements are found on the . . . . . . . . . . . . . . . . .-hand side.

**8** Group VII (the . . . . . . . . . . . . . . . . . ) become . . . . . . . . . . . . . . . . . reactive from the top to the bottom of the group.

**9** Alkali metals react vigorously with water to give . . . . . . . . . . . . . . . . . solutions and the gas . . . . . . . . . . . . . . . . .

**10** Complete the following table.

| *Element/compound* | *Symbol/formula* | *Use* |
|---|---|---|
| Helium | (a) . . . . . . . . . . . . . . . | (b) . . . . . . . . . . . . . . . . . . . . . . |
| (c) . . . . . . . . . . . . . . . | NaOH | Drain cleaner |
| (d) . . . . . . . . . . . . . . . | (e) . . . . . . . . . . . . . . . | Electrical wiring, water pipes |
| Chlorine | (f) . . . . . . . . . . . . . . . | (g) . . . . . . . . . . . . . . . . . . . . . . |
| (h) . . . . . . . . . . . . . . . | NaClO | (i) . . . . . . . . . . . . . . . . . . . . . . |

## PRACTICE QUESTIONS

***Question 1 – Foundation***

You will find the Periodic Table in the Data Section (on p. 120) useful in answering this question.

(a) Give the names of two alkali metals.

. . . . . . . . . . . . . . . . . . . . . . . . . . . . . . . . . . . . . . . . . . . . . . . . . . . . . . . . . [2]

(b) There is a group of reactive non-metals in the Periodic Table.

(i) What is the number of this group? . . . . . . . . . . . . . . . . . . . . . . . . . . . [1]

(ii) What is the name given to this group of elements? . . . . . . . . . . . . . . . . [1]

(iii) Give the names of **two** elements in this group. . . . . . . . . . . . . . . . . . . . [2]

(c) There is a group of unreactive non-metals in the Periodic Table.

(i) What is the name given to this group of elements? . . . . . . . . . . . . . . . . [1]

(ii) Name **one** element in this group . . . . . . . . . . . . . . . . . . . . . . . . . . . [1]

(d) Sodium and rubidium are in the same group of the Periodic Table. Sodium is near the top of the group and rubidium is near the bottom.

(i) Generally, how does the reactivity of rubidium compare with that of sodium? .............................................. [1]

(ii) The formula of sodium carbonate is $Na_2CO_3$. What is the formula of rubidium carbonate? .............................................. [1]

(e) A metal **M** is in Group III of the Periodic Table. Write down the formula of

(i) the chloride of M .............................................. [1]

(ii) the oxide of M .............................................. [1]

**Total: 12 marks**

(NICCEA)

***Question 2 – Higher***

Use the table below to answer the questions which follow.

Figure 2.9

| *Group* / *Period* | *I* | *II* | *III* | *IV* | *V* | *VI* | *VII* | *0* |
|---|---|---|---|---|---|---|---|---|
| **2** | Li | | B | C | | | F | |
| **3** | Na | | Al | Si | P | | Cl | |
| **4** | K | Ca | | Ge | | | Br | |
| **5** | Rb | | | | | | I | |

(a) On a separate sheet of plain paper, show diagrammatically the electronic configuration of an atom of:

(i) aluminium (ii) phosphorus. [4]

(b) Which element in Group VII reacts most vigorously with sodium?

.............................................. [1]

(c) A student passed some chlorine into a solution of potassium bromide.

(i) What would be observed? .............................................. [1]

(ii) Write a balanced symbol equation for this reaction.

.............................................. [2]

(d) On a separate sheet of plain paper, draw a diagram to show the arrangement of electrons in a chlorine molecule. Show outer-shell electrons only. [3]

(e) In the Periodic Table calcium (Ca) is in Group II and germanium (Ge), is in Group IV. The two elements are in the same period. Write the formula for:

(i) calcium chloride .............................................. [1]

(ii) germanium chloride .............................................. [1]

(f) Elements can be broadly classified as metals and non-metals.

(i) Name **one** element that is classified as a semi-metal .................. [1]

(ii) Name **one** non-metallic element which conducts electricity and explain why it conducts.

Non-metal .............................................. [1]

Explanation ..............................................

.............................................. [2]

**Total: 17 marks**

(NICCEA)

***Question 3 – Higher***

The element magnesium (atomic number 12) reacts with chlorine (atomic number 17) to form the compound magnesium chloride, $MgCl_2$.

(a) Give the meaning of each of the following words:

Element ..................................................................

.................................................................. [1]

Compound ..............................................................

.................................................................. [1]

(b) Complete the diagrams to show the arrangement of electrons in a magnesium atom and in a chlorine atom. [2]

*Figure 2.10*

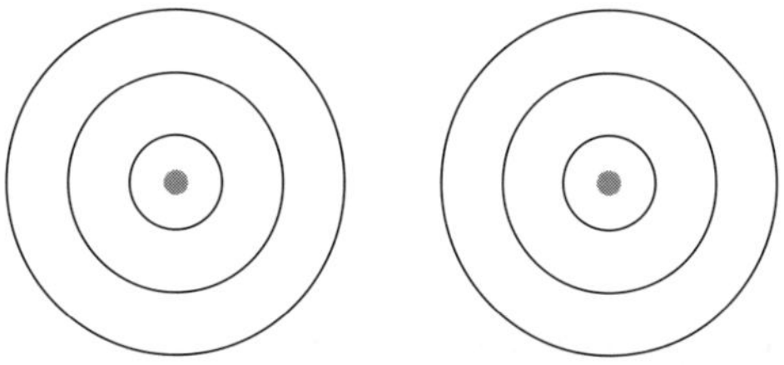

Magnesium atom (Mg)

Chlorine atom (Cl)

(c) What happens to these electron arrangements when magnesium reacts with chlorine to form magnesium chloride, $MgCl_2$?

..................................................................

..................................................................

..................................................................

..................................................................

..................................................................

.................................................................. [4]

(d) The compound magnesium chloride has *ionic* bonding. Explain what this means. ..................................................................

..................................................................

.................................................................. [2]

**Total: 10 marks**

(SEG)

***Question 4 – Foundation***

The positions of the first 20 elements in the Periodic Table are shown below.

*Figure 2.11*

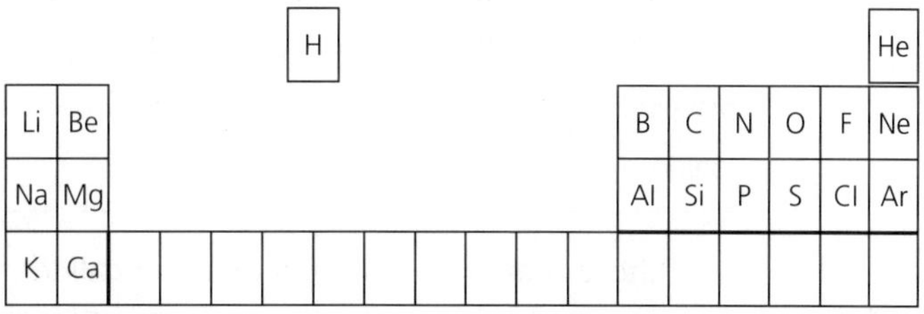

H He

Li Be B C N O F Ne

Na Mg Al Si P S Cl Ar

K Ca

(a) (i) Give the symbol or name of an element in the same **period** as boron, B.

.................................................................. [1]

(ii) Give the symbol or name of an element in the same **group** as calcium, Ca.

.................................................................. [1]

(b) (i) Complete the following table about the halogens. [3]

Figure 2.12

| *Name of halogen* | *Symbol* | *State at room temperature* | *Colour* |
| --- | --- | --- | --- |
| Chlorine | ...... | ...................... | ......... |
| Bromine | Br | Liquid | Red |
| Iodine | I | Solid | Black |

(ii) Give one use of chlorine

........................................................... [1]

(iii) The halogens have similar chemical properties. Explain why.

...........................................................

...........................................................

...........................................................

........................................................... [2]

(c) The diagrams show the electron arrangements of the atoms of two different elements M and Z.

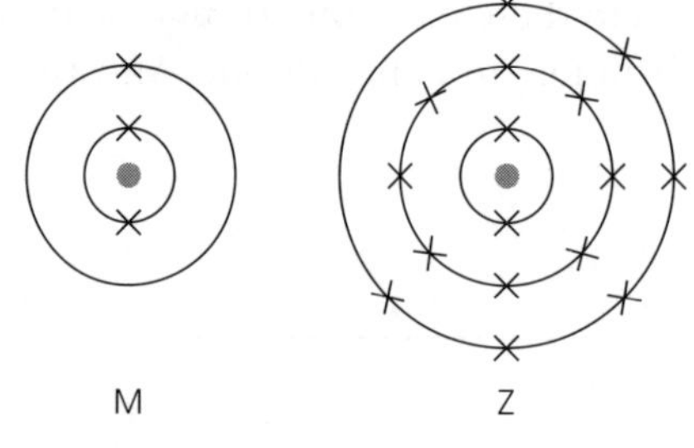


Figure 2.13

Give the symbol or name of element M and element Z. [2]

Element M is .................... Element Z is ....................

(d) Why are the noble gases helium, neon and argon **unreactive**?

........................................................... [1]

**Total: 11 marks**
(SEG)

***Question 5 – Higher***

NOTE
*This question has a student answer with examiner's comments on p. 91.*

(a) Chlorine, bromine and iodine are three of the halogen elements that occur in Group VII of the Periodic Table. The following table gives some data for these elements.

| *Element* | *Melting point °C* | *Boiling point °C* |
| --- | --- | --- |
| Chlorine | −101 | −35 |
| Bromine | −7 | 59 |
| Iodine | 114 | 184 |

(i) There is another halogen element called astatine which has a higher atomic number and follows iodine in Group VII. It is very unstable. Would you expect astatine to be a gas, liquid or solid at room temperature (20 °C)? ........................................ [1]

(ii) Which is the **most** reactive of the three halogens shown in the table?

........................................................... [1]

(iii) Chlorine is a toxic (poisonous) substance, but is used on a large scale in the purification of public water supplies. Write a brief explanation of this.

. . . . . . . . . . . . . . . . . . . . . . . . . . . . . . . . . . . . . . . . . . . . . . . .

. . . . . . . . . . . . . . . . . . . . . . . . . . . . . . . . . . . . . . . . . . . . . . . . [2]

(b) The atoms of the elements hydrogen, chlorine and sodium are represented by the symbols: ${}^{1}_{1}H$, ${}^{35}_{17}Cl$, ${}^{23}_{11}Na$ respectively. Give the electronic structure of hydrogen, chlorine and sodium.

Hydrogen . . . . . . . . . . . . . . . . . . . . . . . . . . . . . . . . . . . . . . . . . . . .

Chlorine . . . . . . . . . . . . . . . . . . . . . . . . . . . . . . . . . . . . . . . . . . . . .

Sodium . . . . . . . . . . . . . . . . . . . . . . . . . . . . . . . . . . . . . . . . . . . . . [3]

(c) Under certain conditions, both hydrogen and sodium react vigorously with chlorine to form hydrogen chloride (HCl) and sodium chloride (NaCl) respectively.

(i) Give the electronic structure of hydrogen chloride.

(ii) Show the electronic changes that take place during the formation of sodium chloride, including the structure of the product.

[3]

(d) Write down, with a reason, whether the structure of sodium chloride is classified as a simple molecule or a giant structure.

. . . . . . . . . . . . . . . . . . . . . . . . . . . . . . . . . . . . . . . . . . . . . . . . .

. . . . . . . . . . . . . . . . . . . . . . . . . . . . . . . . . . . . . . . . . . . . . . . . [2]

# 3 Organic Chemistry

## REVISION TIPS

- Learn the names of the first six alkanes; the following mnemonic may help:

| **M**any | **E**lephants | **P**ass | **B**y | **P**ublic | **H**ouses |
|---|---|---|---|---|---|
| **M**ethane | **E**thane | **P**ropane | **B**utane | **P**entane | **H**exane |
| $CH_4$ | $C_2H_6$ | $C_3H_8$ | $C_4H_{10}$ | $C_5H_{12}$ | $C_6H_{14}$ |

- Learn also the name endings of the following homologous series:

| ***Homologous series*** | alkanes | alkenes | alcohols | carboxylic acids |
|---|---|---|---|---|
| | $C_nH_{2n+2}$ | $C_nH_{2n}$ | $C_nH_{2n+1}OH$ | $C_nH_{2n+1}CO_2H$ |
| ***Name ending*** | -ane | -ene | -anol | -anoic acid |

- From the names of the alkanes and the functional group endings you will be able to name all the organic compounds that you will be tested on. Thus the names of the following compounds are:

| ***Formula*** | ***No of carbon atoms*** | ***Start of name*** | ***Homologous series*** | ***Name*** |
|---|---|---|---|---|
| $C_2H_6$ | 2 | eth- | -ane | Ethane |
| $C_3H_6$ | 3 | prop- | -ene | Propene |
| $CH_3OH$ | 1 | meth- | -anol | Methanol |
| $CH_3CO_2H$ | 2* | eth- | -anoic | Ethanoic acid |

**Note*: $CH_3CO_2H$ has 2 carbon atoms

- Learn the general properties of each homologous series.
- Remember that **saturated** compounds undergo **addition** reactions and that **unsaturated** compounds undergo **substitution** reactions.
- Do not confuse **isomers** (same molecular formula, different structural formulae) with **isotopes** (same number of protons, different number of neutrons).
- Polymers are named from their monomers; propene polymerises to poly(propene).

## TOPIC OUTLINE

### Key definitions

- A **fuel** is any substance that produces energy when it burns. Many organic compounds are fuels such as hydrocarbons and alcohols.
- **Volatile** liquids easily turn from liquids to vapours at room temperature because they have very low boiling points, e.g. petrol is a volatile liquid.
- **Hydrocarbons** are compounds of carbon and hydrogen ONLY, e.g. octane $C_8H_{18}$.

- **Homologous series** are compounds with the same general formula and similar chemical properties, e.g. alkanes ($C_nH_{2n+2}$)
- **Isomers** are compounds with the same molecular formula but different structural formula, e.g. there are two isomers of formula $C_4H_{10}$ – butane and 2-methylpropane.
- **Saturated compounds** contain no double or triple bonds between the carbon-carbon atoms, e.g. ethane $H_3C{-}CH_3$ is saturated.
- **Unsaturated compounds** contain either carbon-carbon double bonds or carbon-carbon triple bonds, e.g. ethene $H_2C{=}CH_2$ and ethyne $HC{\equiv}CH$. They undergo **addition reactions** (see below).
- An **addition reaction** is a reaction in which two or more molecules react together to form **one** molecule only, e.g. $C_2H_4 + Br_2 \rightarrow C_2H_4Br_2$.
- A **polymer** is a long chain molecule formed by the joining together of many very small molecules called monomers, e.g. monomer–propene; polymer–poly(propene).
- **Cracking** is the process of breaking large molecules of hydrocarbons into smaller hydrocarbon molecules, e.g. decane ($C_{10}H_{22}$) to octane ($C_8H_{18}$) and ethene ($C_2H_4$). One of the products is always unsaturated.

## Fuels

- **Fossil fuels** are fuels that came from living matter millions of years ago. They include coal, peat, lignite, petroleum and natural gas – these are **non-renewable energy** sources.
- Fuels such as wood can be grown over a relatively short period of time – these are **renewable energy** sources.
- Petroleum can be fractionally distilled to give the products shown in Figure 3.1.

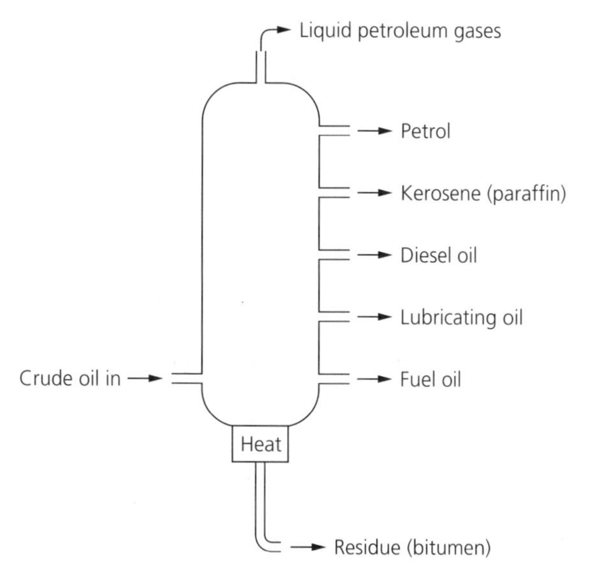


*Figure 3.1* Fractional distillation of petroleum

## Combustion of hydrocarbons

All hydrocarbons burn in excess air to give carbon dioxide and water. If a limited supply of air is used, carbon monoxide and water are formed.

In excess air $CH_4(g) + 2O_2(g) \rightarrow CO_2(g) + H_2O(l)$

In a limited supply of air $2CH_4(g) + 3O_2(g) \rightarrow 2CO(g) + 4H_2O(l)$

## Homologous series

Organic compounds in the same homologous series:

- can be represented by a general formula,
- have similar chemical properties,

- are made by similar reactions, and
- show a regular change in their physical properties

Ethene $C_2H_4$ (−104 °C), propene $C_3H_6$ (−48 °C) and butene $C_4H_8$ (−6.2 °C) are all in the same homologous series called the **alkenes**. The numbers in brackets are the boiling points of the alkenes. These are in the same homologous series because

- they can be represented by a general formula $C_nH_{2n}$;
- they all decolourise bromine water because they are unsaturated;
- they are made by dehydrating the corresponding alcohol;

$C_nH_{2n+1}OH \rightarrow C_nH_{2n} + H_2O$

- the boiling points increase regularly with increasing molecular size.

HINT
*$CH_2$ does not exist, so the first member of this series is $C_2H_4$.*

You should be able to predict these properties of the next member of the series, pentene: it will have a formula $C_5H_{10}$; decolourise bromine water; be made by dehydrating $C_5H_{11}OH$ (pentanol) and its boiling point will be about 34 °C (in fact it is 30 °C).

## Isomers

The boiling point of isomers decreases as branching increases.

```
                                       H                        H
                                       |                        |
                                     H-C-H                    H-C-H
   H  H  H  H  H                     H |  H  H                H |  H
   |  |  |  |  |                     | |  |  |                | |  |
 H-C--C--C--C--C-H                 H-C-C--C--C-H            H-C-C--C-H
   |  |  |  |  |                     | |  |  |                | |  |
   H  H  H  H  H                     H H  H  H                H |  H
                                                              H-C-H
                                                                |
                                                                H
```

*Figure 3.2*

**pentane** (36.3 °C); **2-methylbutane** (27.9 °C); **2,2-dimethylpropane** (9.5 °C)

## Unsaturated compounds

HINT
*Other substances, including water, iodine and chlorine also undergo addition reactions with unsaturated compounds.*

The test for **unsaturation** is to shake the compound with bromine water; if the bromine water is decolourised (from orange to colourless), then the compound is unsaturated.

Remember that unsaturated compounds undergo **addition reactions**. This is an example of addition reaction.

$C_3H_6(g) + Br_2 \rightarrow C_3H_6Br_2$

## Polymers

HINT
*Monomers and addition polymers have the same empirical formula.*

Large number of **monomers** join together by addition reactions to form **polymers**.

| ***Monomer*** | ***Formula*** | ***Polymer*** | ***Formula*** | ***Uses*** |
|---|---|---|---|---|
| Ethene | $H_2C{=}CH_2$ | Poly(ethene) | $(H_2C{-}CH_2)_n$ | Food wrapping, bags, electrical wire insulation |
| Vinyl Chloride | $H_2C{=}CHCl$ | Poly(vinyl chloride) | $(H_2C{-}CHCl)_n$ | Raincoats, artificial leather, electrical wire insulation |
| Propene | $H_3CHC{=}CH_2$ | Poly(propene) | $(H_3CHCCH_2)_n$ | Moulded chairs, carpets |

Polymers are of two types: **thermosoftening** and **thermosetting**.

- Thermosoftening polymers can be heated to soften them and then reshaped, e.g. PVC and perspex.
- Thermosetting polymers cannot be melted once they are formed, e.g. araldite, bakelite and melamine.

Study the table below, it compares the use of polymers with 'old' substances.

| ***Everyday object*** | ***Polymer*** | ***'Old' material*** | ***Advantage of polymer*** | ***Disadvantage of polymer*** |
|---|---|---|---|---|
| Bowl | Polythene | Steel | Light | Scratches |
| Drain pipe | PVC | Cast iron | Does not corrode | Breaks easily |
| Lunch box | Poly(styrene) | Aluminium | Light, cheap | Scratches |
| Rope | Nylon | Jute | Stronger | More elastic |
| Windows | Perspex | Glass | Less brittle | Scratches |

One of the main problems with plastics is that they are **non-biodegradable**. When we throw away plastics or bury them, they do not decompose.

## Cracking

HINT
*Cracking can produce different products according to the conditions used.*

Some of the fractions from distilling crude oil are broken down into smaller, more useful substances by heating (**thermal cracking**) or heating in the presence of a catalysts (**catalytic cracking**). The products are usually an alkene and an alkane (often hydrogen is also formed).

*Example*
Decane ($C_{10}H_{22}$) can be cracked to produce octane ($C_8H_{18}$) and ethene ($C_2H_4$).

$C_{10}H_{22} \rightarrow C_8H_{18}$ (octane) + $C_2H_4$ (ethene)

## Alcohols

Alcohols have the general formula $C_nH_{2n+1}OH$.

- They burn in excess oxygen to give carbon dioxide and water (some alcohols such as ethanol are in common use as fuels).
- They are oxidised to carboxylic acids (this is the reason why drinks that contain ethanol taste bitter (acidic) after a period of time – the ethanol is oxidised to ethanoic acid)).
- They react with acids to form esters.
- They react with sodium to give hydrogen.
- They are dehydrated by concentrated sulphuric acid to give an alkene.

## Carboxylic acids

Carboxylic acids have the general formula $C_nH_{2n+1}CO_2H$. They are typical weak acids.

- They have a $pH < 7$.
- They react with metals to give hydrogen.
- They react with bases to form a salt and water.
- They react with carbonate to give carbon dioxide, a salt and water.

A typical organic property is that they react with alcohols to give an ester and water.

## Soaps

Soaps are made by reacting vegetable oils or animal fats with an alkali. Soaps reduce the surface tension of water thus soapy water wets clothes more thoroughly than water on its own.

## REVISION ACTIVITIES

**1** Fill in the missing word.

(a) A compound containing carbon and hydrogen only is called a . . . . . . . . . .

(b) An . . . . . . . . . . . . . . . . . . compound decolourises bromine water.

(c) Thermal . . . . . . . . . . . . . . . . . . is the process of breaking large molecules into smaller molecules by the action of heat.

(d) acid + alcohol → . . . . . . . . . . . . . . . . . . + water.

(e) An . . . . . . . . . . . . . . . . . . reaction occurs when two or more molecules react together to form one molecule.

**2** Name the following substances:

(a) $C_4H_{10}$ . . . . . . . . . . . . . . . . . . . . (b) $C_3H_6$ . . . . . . . . . . . . . . . . . . . . .

(c) $CH_3OH$ . . . . . . . . . . . . . . . . . . . (d) $HCO_2H$ . . . . . . . . . . . . . . . . . .

**3** Write the formula of the following compounds:

(a) methane . . . . . . . . . . . . . . . . . . (b) ethene . . . . . . . . . . . . . . . . . . . . .

(c) propanol . . . . . . . . . . . . . . . . . . (d) ethanoic acid . . . . . . . . . . . . . . . .

**4** Using only the substances listed below:

**butene ethane ethanol methanoic acid poly(styrene) propane sugar**

Name the following.

(a) Two substances in the same homologous series . . . . . . . . . . . . . . . . . . . . .

(b) Four hydrocarbons . . . . . . . . . . . . . . . . . . . . . . . . . . . . . . . . . . . . . . . .

(c) A substance that decolourises bromine water . . . . . . . . . . . . . . . . . . . . . . .

(d) A plastic (polymer) . . . . . . . . . . . . . . . . . . . . . . . . . . . . . . . . . . . . . . . .

(e) A substance made by fermentation . . . . . . . . . . . . . . . . . . . . . . . . . . . . .

(f) A carbohydrate . . . . . . . . . . . . . . . . . . . . . . . . . . . . . . . . . . . . . . . . . .

(g) A substance containing one carbon atom . . . . . . . . . . . . . . . . . . . . . . . . .

**5** (a) What name is given to substances that have the same molecular formula but different structural formulae? . . . . . . . . . . . . . . . . . . . . . . . . . . . . . . .

(b) Draw the structural formula of:
(i) two compounds of molecular formula $C_4H_{10}$
(ii) three compounds of molecular formula $C_5H_{12}$

**6** (a) Propene is an unsaturated hydrocarbon. How would you show that propene was unsaturated? . . . . . . . . . . . . . . . . . . . . . . . . . . . . . . . . . . . . . .

(b) Draw the full structural formula of propene. What part of the structure shows that propene is unsaturated? . . . . . . . . . . . . . . . . . . . . . . . . . . . . . . .

(c) Name the product formed when propene:

(i) reacts with water . . . . . . . . . . . . . . (ii) polymerises . . . . . . . . . . . . . .

**7** (a) Name the process by which crude oil is separated into its various components. ..................................................

..................................................

(b) Name three liquid products obtained from crude oil and give a use for each of these products. ..................................................

..................................................

(c) What is the name given to the process that is used to break down large saturated molecules into smaller molecules? Why is this reaction important? ..................................................

..................................................

**8** Soap is made by warming glyceryl stearate with sodium hydroxide.
(a) Complete the equation:

glyceryl stearate + sodium hydroxide → glycerine + ...............

(b) What name is give to this special type of hydrolysis reaction? ...........

..................................................

(c) Sodium hydroxide is an alkali. What class of organic compound is glyceryl stearate? ..................................................

(d) Suggest a reason for adding a saturated solution of sodium chloride to the mixture once the reaction has finished. ..........................

..................................................

## PRACTICE QUESTIONS

***Question 1 – Foundation***

The hydrocarbons methane ($CH_4$), butane ($C_4H_{10}$) and octane are members of the same homologous series.

(a) (i) What is meant by a hydrocarbon?

.................................................. [1]

(ii) Name a raw material rich in hydrocarbons.

.................................................. [1]

(b) State **two** general characteristics of any homologous series.

..................................................

..................................................

..................................................

.................................................. [2]

(c) There are eight carbon atoms in one molecule of octane. How many hydrogen atoms are present?

.................................................. [1]

**Total: 5 marks**
(MEG)

### Question 2

(a) (**Foundation**) The table below shows the formula for some monomers and their corresponding polymers.

Figure 3.3

| *Monomer* | *Structural formula* | *Polymer* | *Structural formula* |
|---|---|---|---|
| Ethene | | Poly(ethene) | [ H H<br>\| \|<br>—C—C—<br>\| \|<br>H H ]$_n$ |
| Chloroethene | H Cl<br>\| \|<br>C=C<br>\| \|<br>H H | Poly(chloroethene) | [ H Cl<br>\| \|<br>—C—C—<br>\| \|<br>H H ]$_n$ |
| Propene | $CH_3$ H<br>\| \|<br>C=C<br>\| \|<br>H H | | [ $CH_3$ H<br>\| \|<br>—C—C—<br>\| \|<br>H H ]$_n$ |
| Tetrafluoroethene | F F<br>\| \|<br>C=C<br>\| \|<br>F F | Poly(tetrafluoroethene) | |

(i) Complete the table. [3]

(ii) Name **one** monomer from the table which is a hydrocarbon ..........

.............................................................. [1]

(iii) What is the similarity between the structural formulae of the monomers?

.............................................................. [1]

(iv) Write down the molecular formula of tetrafluoroethene ..........

.............................................................. [1]

(v) Poly(ethene) is used for many purposes instead of metals. Give one example where it is an advantage to use poly(ethene) instead of metal.

..............................................................

.............................................................. [1]

(b) (**Higher**)
A waste disposal company wanted to separate industrial waste. The waste contained iron and steel, polymers, paper and other metals. The table shows details about what happens when these materials are added to water.

| *Material* | *What happens in water* |
|---|---|
| Iron and steel | Sink |
| Polymers | Float |
| Paper | Floats and then sinks when saturated with water |
| Other materials | Sink |

(i) How could polymers be separated from industrial waste?

.............................................................. [1]

(ii) Suggest how iron and steel can be separated from other materials.

. . . . . . . . . . . . . . . . . . . . . . . . . . . . . . . . . . . . . . . . . . . . . . . . . . . . . . .

. . . . . . . . . . . . . . . . . . . . . . . . . . . . . . . . . . . . . . . . . . . . . . . . . . . . [1]

**Total: 9 marks**
(MEG)

NOTE
*This question has a student answer with examiner's comments.* *See p. 93.*

***Question 3 – Higher***

(a) An important process used in the petrochemical industry is called *cracking*. The products are used as fuels or chemical feedstocks (petrochemicals). An example of this process is given in the following equation, for the cracking of decane to give octane and ethene, which are described as being saturated and unsaturated hydrocarbons respectively.

$C_{10}H_{22}(l) \rightarrow C_8H_{18}(l) + C_2H_4(g)$

(i) What do the symbols (l) and (g) mean in the above equation?

. . . . . . . . . . . . . . . . . . . . . . . . . . . . . . . . . . . . . . . . . . . . . . . . . . . . [1]

(ii) What is the difference between a saturated and an unsaturated hydrocarbon?

. . . . . . . . . . . . . . . . . . . . . . . . . . . . . . . . . . . . . . . . . . . . . . . . . . . . [1]

(b) Ethene undergoes addition polymerisation to form poly(ethene) (polythene), which is a plastic.

(i) Write down what is meant by polymerisation.

. . . . . . . . . . . . . . . . . . . . . . . . . . . . . . . . . . . . . . . . . . . . . . . . . . . . . . .

. . . . . . . . . . . . . . . . . . . . . . . . . . . . . . . . . . . . . . . . . . . . . . . . . . . . [2]

(ii) Give a symbol equation for the reaction occurring in the addition polymerisation of ethene.

. . . . . . . . . . . . . . . . . . . . . . . . . . . . . . . . . . . . . . . . . . . . . . . . . . . . [2]

(iii) Give **one** use of poly(ethene) (polythene).

. . . . . . . . . . . . . . . . . . . . . . . . . . . . . . . . . . . . . . . . . . . . . . . . . . . . [1]

(c) The table below gives some information about four different plastics, **A**, **B**, **C** and **D**.

| | *Effect of heat* | *Flexibility* | *Hardness* | *Colour* |
|---|---|---|---|---|
| **A** | Melts | Brittle | Soft | White |
| **B** | Melts | Very flexible | Soft | White |
| **C** | Melts | Brittle | Hard | Transparent |
| **D** | Stable | Brittle | Hard | Various |

Write down which plastic you would choose for making (i) a plastic shopping bag and (ii) a fish bowl, giving **one** reason in each case.

. . . . . . . . . . . . . . . . . . . . . . . . . . . . . . . . . . . . . . . . . . . . . . . . . . . . [2]

. . . . . . . . . . . . . . . . . . . . . . . . . . . . . . . . . . . . . . . . . . . . . . . . . . . . [2]

**Total: 11 marks**
(WJEC)

# 4 Industrial Chemistry and electrolysis

## REVISION TIPS

***Metal extraction and purification***

- Draw neat, fully labelled, diagrams of the following.
  - The **aluminium** electrolysis cell.
  - **Iron** extraction in the blast furnace.
  - The cell for **copper** purification by electrolysis.

  Include equations for the main reactions.
- Learn why aluminium is extracted by electrolysis whereas iron is extracted by carbon-reduction. The definitions of oxidation and reduction can be remembered by **OIL RIG: O**xidation **I**s **L**oss and **R**eduction **I**s **G**ain – of electrons.

***Manufacture of important non-metallic compounds***

- Summarise, in numbered steps with equations, the manufacture of the following.
  - Ammonia from nitrogen and hydrogen in the **Haber process**.
  - Sulphuric acid from sulphur in the **Contact process**.
  - Nitric acid by oxidation of ammonia (NICCEA Higher only)
  - Quicklime in a lime-kiln.
  - Chlorine and sodium hydroxide by electrolysis of brine.
  - Bromine from sea water (MEG Higher only).
- Learn the **explanations for the reactions** occurring in all of these industrial processes.
- Draw up lists of the major uses of:
  - ammonia
  - sulphuric acid
  - chlorine
  - lime
- Learn how **fertilisers** are made from ammonia and from sulphuric acid.
- Study and understand the principles of electrolysis and its industrial application, e.g. **electroplating**.

## TOPIC OUTLINE

### Key definitions

- **Metal extraction** involves the reduction of ores to the metal.
- **Reduction** of oxide ores is the removal of oxygen from a compound, e.g.

  $Fe_2O_3 + 3CO \rightarrow 2Fe + 3CO_2$

  In electrolysis, reduction occurs at the cathode and is the addition of electrons to metal ions, e.g.

  $Al^{3+} + 3e^- \rightarrow Al$
- **Oxidation** is the addition of oxygen to a substance, e.g.

  $C + O_2 \rightarrow CO_2$

  or the removal of electrons from an atom, molecule or ion, e.g. in electrolysis at the anode

  $2Cl^- \rightarrow Cl_2 + 2e^-$

- **Electrolysis** is the decomposition of a compound in a molten state or in solution, by a direct electric current.
- **Ores** are concentrated minerals that are profitable to extract, e.g. bauxite, $Al_2O_3$, is the major aluminium ore.
- **Alloys** are solid mixtures of metals with other elements, usually metals. Alloying creates a wider range of properties than are found in pure metals, e.g. carbon steels.
- **Catalysts** are substances capable of increasing the rate of a reaction without being consumed in the process, e.g. iron in the Haber process.

## Metal extraction and purification

### *Aluminium extraction*

- Aluminium is found as the ore **bauxite** which, when purified, gives alumina, $Al_2O_3$. It is not possible to extract aluminium from alumina by carbon reduction – electrolysis must be used, see Figure 4.1.

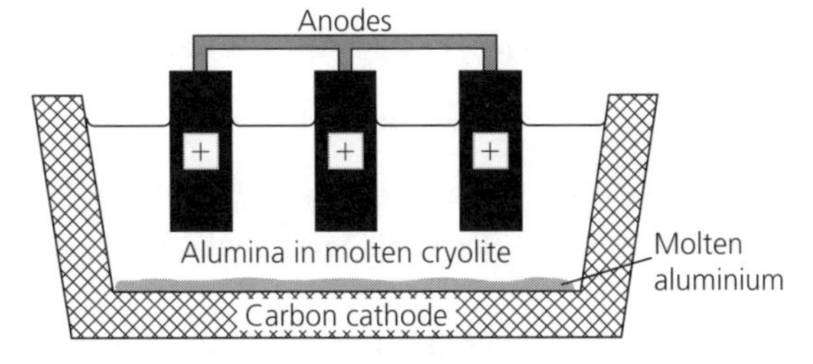


*Figure 4.1* Aluminium extraction by electrolysis

- **Alumina** melts at about 2000 °C but electrolysis can be carried out at 1000 °C by *dissolving* the alumina in **molten cryolite**, thus saving energy. The cathode reaction is:

$Al^{3+}(l) + 3e^- \rightarrow Al(l)$ (siphoned off daily)

The anode reaction forms oxygen gas which **oxidises** the carbon anode:

$2O^{2-} \rightarrow O_2 + 4e^-$ followed by $C + O_2 \rightarrow CO_2$

HINT
*Anodes must be replaced at intervals as they burn away.*

### *Iron extraction*

- Iron is found commonly as iron (III) oxide, $Fe_2O_3$, in the ore **haematite**. Iron oxide is reduced by carbon in a blast furnace, see Figure 4.2.

Iron ore, coke and limestone
Hot, waste-gases CO, $CO_2$, $N_2$ and Ar
700 °C
**1.** $C + O_2 \rightarrow CO_2$
**3.** $3CO + Fe_2O_3 \rightarrow 2Fe + 3CO_2$
**2.** $C + CO_2 \rightarrow 2CO$
Hot air
18000 °C
Hot air
Molten slag
Molten iron

*Figure 4.2* A blast furnace

- Equations 1–3 show the reactions that occur in the production of iron.
- **Limestone** decomposes in the furnace to form calcium oxide. Calcium oxide reacts with silica(sand) in the ore forming slag.

$CaO + SiO_2 \rightarrow CaSiO_3$ (calcium silicate – glasslike slag)

- Reactions 1 and 3 in the furnace are **exothermic** so waste gases are hot and are used to preheat the air blast, thus saving heat energy.

***Steel making***

HINT
*Steel making is a major use of oxygen.*

- **Oxygen** is blown through molten iron from the blast furnace. The **carbon** content is reduced to the required value for mild steel (0.1–0.25%), medium-carbon (0.25–0.5%) or high-carbon (0.5–1.5%) steel.
- If **alloy steels** are required the appropriate alloying metal(s) is added – manganese (railway points), vanadium (screwdrivers), tungsten (drill bits), chromium and nickel (stainless steel).

***Copper refining***

- Impure copper is purified by electrolysis using an impure copper anode and a pure copper cathode in a solution of copper sulphate.
- Copper dissolves from the anode as copper ions:

$Cu(s) \rightarrow Cu^{2+}(aq) + 2e^-$

- Copper (99.99% pure) deposits on the cathode:

$Cu^{2+}(aq) + 2e^- \rightarrow Cu(s)$

- Copper that dissolves from the anode eventually deposits on the cathode so the concentration of the electrolyte remains unchanged during the process.

## Properties and uses of aluminium, iron and copper

Figure 4.3

| *Metal* | *Properties* | *Use* |
|---|---|---|
| Aluminium | Low density, strong, resists corrosion, good heat and electricity conductor. | Aircraft parts, pans, drinks cans, electrical cable, window frames. |
| Iron (steel) | Tough, easily shaped, magnetic, alloys readily, cheap. | Constructional work in buildings, railways, cars, bridges. Magnets. |
| Copper | Easily shaped, good conductor of heat and electricity. | Electrical wiring, circuit boards: heating pipes and cisterns: brass/ bronze. |

## Manufacture of non-metallic compounds and their uses

***Sulphuric acid manufacture by the Contact process***

Sulphuric acid is made from **elemental sulphur** as follows:

- Sulphur is burnt in air to become sulphur dioxide:

$S(s) + O_2(g) \rightarrow SO_2(g)$

- Sulphur dioxide is **catalytically oxidised** to become sulphur trioxide. This part is the Contact process:

$2SO_2(g) + O_2(g) \rightleftharpoons 2SO_3(g)$

- **Catalyst**: vanadium(V) oxide; **temperature**: 450 °C; **pressure**: normal.

KEY POINT
*The high temperature ensures fast reaction. Excess air is used so the yield is high even at normal pressure (see Chapter 6).*

- Sulphur trioxide is dissolved in concentrated sulphuric acid:

$SO_3 + H_2SO_4 \rightarrow H_2S_2O_7$ **(oleum)**

- The oleum formed is diluted with water to make 98% sulphuric acid:

  $H_2O + H_2S_2O_7 \rightarrow 2H_2SO_4$

HINT
*'Pickling' is the neutralisation of rust (a base) by dipping in acid.*

*Uses of sulphuric acid*
Car-battery acid, manufacture of fertiliser, paint, detergents, plastics and fibres: steel 'pickling'.

***Ammonia manufacture by the Haber (-Bosch) process***
Ammonia is made from **nitrogen** (from the air) and **hydrogen** (from cracking oil or the reaction of natural gas (methane) with steam) as follows:

- A mixture of hydrogen and nitrogen in the ratio of **3:1** is passed over a catalyst in the reactor:

  $3H_2(g) + N_2(g) \rightleftarrows 2NH_3(g)$

- **Catalyst**: iron; **temperature**: 450 °C; **pressure**: 200 atmospheres

KEY POINT
*The high pressure moves the equilibrium to the right; the high temperature does the opposite* but *is needed to speed up the reaction (see Chapter 6).*

- When **equilibrium** is reached the product contains about **15%** of ammonia. Ammonia is extracted by **liquifying** it. The unused nitrogen and hydrogen is recycled.

*Uses of ammonia*
Mainly used to make fertiliser, nitric acid and nylon.

***Nitric acid manufacture***
Ammonia is oxidised to make nitric acid as follows:

- Ammonia is first oxidised to nitrogen monoxide:

  $4NH_3(g) + 5O_2(g) \xrightarrow[\text{platinum catalyst}]{850\,°C} 4NO(g) + 6H_2O(g)$

- Nitrogen monoxide oxidises further to nitrogen dioxide

  $4NO(g) + 2O_2(g) \rightarrow 4NO_2(g)$

- Nitrogen dioxide then reacts with water and more oxygen to form nitric acid.

  $4NO_2(g) + 2H_2O(l) + O_2(g) \rightarrow 4HNO_3(aq)$

*Uses of nitric acid*
Nitric acid is used to make ammonium nitrate and synthetic fibres.

***Fertiliser manufacture***
Fertiliser manufacture is a major use of ammonia and nitric acid.

The most common **nitrogenous fertiliser** in use is ammonium nitrate. It is manufactured by neutralising ammonia with nitric acid:

$NH_3(aq) + HNO_3(aq) \rightarrow NH_4NO_3(aq)$

***Bromine manufacture from sea water (MEG only)***

HINT
*Chlorine is more reactive than bromine.*

- Sea water contains bromide ions which can be **oxidised** to bromine by the use of chlorine gas if the conditions are acidic.
- A pH of 3.5 is produced by adding sulphuric acid to the sea water before the chlorine is added.

  $Cl_2(g) + 2Br^-(aq) \rightarrow 2Cl^-(aq) + Br_2(g)$ (in acid solution)

- Bromine gas is blown out of the mixture and condensed.

*Uses of bromine*
It is used to make anti-knock (an additive for leaded petrol) but this is a rapidly declining need.

### *Lime manufacture (CaO) from limestone*

KEY POINT
*Limestone is also used in glassmaking and cement manufacture.*

- Quicklime is made by decomposing limestone at 1000 °C in lime kilns heated by natural gas or coal:

$CaCO_3(s) \rightarrow CaO(s) + CO_2(g)$ (endothermic)

HINT
*The exothermic nature of lime-slaking suggests the reason why quicklime is dangerous to use.*

- Quicklime is usually **slaked** to make it safer to use:

$\underset{\text{quicklime}}{CaO(s)} + H_2O(l) \rightarrow \underset{\text{slaked lime}}{Ca(OH)_2(s)}$ (exothermic)

*Uses of lime*
Slaked lime (lime) is used in steel making to remove acidic impurities, and in agriculture to neutralize soil acidity and in mortar.

### *Electrolysis of brine (NaCl(aq)) in the manufacture of chlorine*

The principles of electrolysis can be applied to the decomposition of brine.
The ions in brine are $H^+$, $OH^-$, $Na^+$ and $Cl^-$. The electrolysis products are:

- **Hydrogen** at the cathode and **chlorine** at the titanium anode:

$2H^+ + 2e^- \rightarrow H_2$ $\quad\quad$ $2Cl^- \rightarrow Cl_2 + 2e^-$

- Sodium hydroxide accumulates around the cathode as undischarged $Na^+$ and $OH^-$ ions and is recovered as an impure solution for industrial use.

*Uses of chlorine and sodium hydroxide*
- Chlorine is used mainly to make PVC . It is also used to sterilise domestic water and to bleach wood pulp to make paper.
- Sodium hydroxide is an important general chemical in industry and is also used to make soap.

## REVISION ACTIVITIES

Fill in the missing word(s)

1 (a) Metals are extracted from concentrated mineral sources called .........

(b) Some metals are found ........... in the ground and are called native.

(c) Extraction of a metal from its oxide ore is an example of ..............

(d) .................... is a common ore of iron with the formula, $Fe_2O_3$.
Iron is extracted from it using ................ as the reducing agent.

(e) Aluminium is extracted from its oxide by the process called
..........................................................

(f) To extract aluminium, its oxide must be dissolved in molten ...........
before being electrolysed. Aluminium is deposited at the ..............

(g) Electrolysis is the . . . . . . . . . . . . . . . . of a compound by passage of a

. . . . . . . . . . . . . . . . . . . . . . . . . . . . . . . . .

(h) Electrolysis is used to purify copper. The cathode reaction is

. . . . . . . . . . . . . . . . $+2e^- \rightarrow$ . . . . . . . . . . . . . . . .

(i) In the Haber process, ammonia is formed when the two elements

. . . . . . . . . . . . . . . . . . . . . . . . and . . . . . . . . . . . . . . . . . . . . . . . . combine at

. . . . . . . . . . . . . . . . . . . °C and . . . . . . . . . . . . . . . . atmospheres pressure

over an . . . . . . . . . . . . . . . . catalyst. The equation is:

. . . . . . . . . . . . . . $N_2 +$ . . . . . . . . . . . . . . . $H_2 \rightleftarrows$ . . . . . . . . . . . . . . . $NH_3$

(j) Ammonia is oxidised by air in the manufacture of . . . . . . . . . . . . . . . . . . . .

**2** Sulphuric acid is manufactured from sulphur in three stages:

(a) The sulphur is oxidised to sulphur dioxide. The equation is:

. . . . . . . . . . . . . . . . + . . . . . . . . . . . . . . . . $\rightarrow$ . . . . . . . . . . . . . . . .

(b) Sulphur dioxide is oxidised to . . . . . . . . . . . . . . . . . The equation is:

$2SO_2(g) + O_2(g) \rightleftarrows 2SO_3(g)$

using a temperature of . . . . . . . . . . . . . . . . °C using a a catalyst of

. . . . . . . . . . . . . . . . (V) . . . . . . . . . . . . . . . . .

(c) Concentrated sulphuric acid is used to dissolve the $SO_3$ to form the compound $H_2S_2O_7$, called . . . . . . . . . . . . . . . . , which is then reacted with water to produce the final product – sulphuric acid of concentration

. . . . . . . . . . . . . . . . %.

**3** Describe, briefly, what occurs in a lime-kiln. Give an equation for the reaction naming the reactants and products.

. . . . . . . . . . . . . . . . . . . . . . . . . . . . . . . . . . . . . . . . . . . . . . . . . . . . . . . . . . . .

. . . . . . . . . . . . . . . . . . . . . . . . . . . . . . . . . . . . . . . . . . . . . . . . . . . . . . . . . . . .

. . . . . . . . . . . . . . . . . . . . . . . . . . . . . . . . . . . . . . . . . . . . . . . . . . . . . . . . . . . .

**4** Give two major uses of each of the following:

(a) Aluminium . . . . . . . . . . . . . . . . . . . . . . . . . . . . . . . . . . . . . . . . . . . . .

(b) Mild steel . . . . . . . . . . . . . . . . . . . . . . . . . . . . . . . . . . . . . . . . . . . . .

(c) Copper . . . . . . . . . . . . . . . . . . . . . . . . . . . . . . . . . . . . . . . . . . . . . . .

(d) Ammonia . . . . . . . . . . . . . . . . . . . . . . . . . . . . . . . . . . . . . . . . . . . . .

(e) Sulphuric acid . . . . . . . . . . . . . . . . . . . . . . . . . . . . . . . . . . . . . . . . .

(f) Nitric acid . . . . . . . . . . . . . . . . . . . . . . . . . . . . . . . . . . . . . . . . . . . .

(g) Lime . . . . . . . . . . . . . . . . . . . . . . . . . . . . . . . . . . . . . . . . . . . . . . . . .

(h) Chlorine . . . . . . . . . . . . . . . . . . . . . . . . . . . . . . . . . . . . . . . . . . . . . .

(i) Bromine . . . . . . . . . . . . . . . . . . . . . . . . . . . . . . . . . . . . . . . . . . . . . .

(j) Sodium hydroxide . . . . . . . . . . . . . . . . . . . . . . . . . . . . . . . . . . . . . .

5 Give a one line definition, with an example, of the terms:

(a) Ore ................................................

(b) Reduction ................................................

(c) Exothermic reaction ................................................

(d) Endothermic reaction ................................................

(e) Equilibrium reaction ................................................

(f) Nitrogenous fertiliser ................................................

(g) Alloy steel ................................................

(h) Cathodic reduction ................................................

(i) Anodic oxidation ................................................

(j) Catalyst ................................................

## PRACTICE QUESTIONS

***Question 1 – Higher***

Ammonia is made by combining nitrogen with hydrogen.

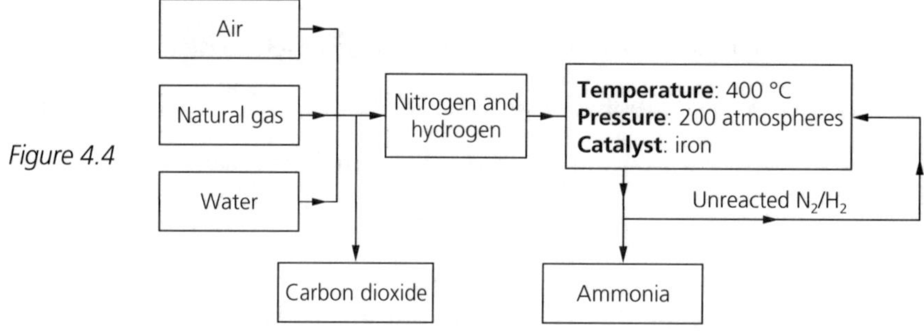


*Figure 4.4*

(a) (i) What are the **two** sources of hydrogen in this diagram?

................................................ [1]

(ii) Carbon dioxide can be removed by reacting the gas with an alkaline solution. Explain why. ................................................

................................................ [1]

(b) (i) Balance the equation for the formation of ammonia.

............. $N_2$ + ............. $H_2 \rightleftarrows$ ............. $NH_3$ [1]

(ii) In this equation, what does the $\rightleftarrows$ represent?

................................................

................................................ [1]

(iii) The rate of reaction to form ammonia is increased by increasing the pressure. Explain why, in terms of the collision theory.

................................................

................................................ [2]

(iv) A catalyst is used in this reaction. The use of the catalyst makes the process more economical. Explain why.

.................................................................

.................................................................

.................................................................

.................................................................

................................................................. [3]

**Total: 9 marks**
(SEG)

***Question 2 – Higher***

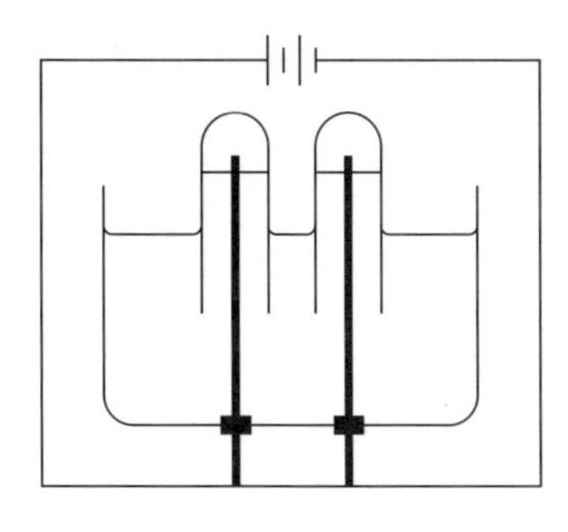

*Figure 4.5*

(a) An experiment to investigate the electrolysis of concentrated sodium chloride solution was set up as shown in the diagram (Fig. 4.5).

(i) What is meant by the term electrolysis?

................................................................. [2]

(ii) What name is given to the negative electrode?

................................................................. [1]

(iii) What is observed at the **anode** during the above electrolysis experiment?

.................................................................

................................................................. [2]

(iv) What is observed at the negative electrode during the above electrolysis experiment? .................................................................

................................................................. [2]

(v) Write a **balanced ionic** equation for the reaction taking place in (**iv**) above. ................................................................. [2]

(b) (i) Impure copper metal can be purified by electrolysis. Describe how this may be carried out.

.................................................................

.................................................................

.................................................................

.................................................................

.................................................................

................................................................. [5]

(ii) Write a **balanced ionic** equation to show the formation of copper in (**b**) (**i**) above. ................................................................. [2]

**Total: 16 marks**
(NICCEA)

## Section B questions (Compulsory in London (Edexcel) questions)

***Question 3 – Foundation***

Describe the manufacture of sulphuric acid from sulphur. Give the necessary conditions at each stage of the process and write word equations for the chemical reactions. Do NOT give details of the chemical plant.

**Total: 10 marks**
(London)

***Question 4 – Higher***

(a) Describe how impure iron from the blast furnace is made into mild steel. explain how the process removes one impurity from the iron and state one effect this has on the properties of the iron. [7]

(b) What is meant by the term **alloy steel**? Give one example of an alloy steel with one of its uses. [3]

**Total: 10 marks**
(London)

***Question 5 – Higher***

Aluminium is the most abundant metal in the Earth's crust. The impure ore of aluminium is found in large quantities in Australia. The impure ore is purified and dissolved in molten cryolite at 900 °C. The mixture is then electrolysed and aluminium is formed at one electrode. The other electrode has to be replaced regularly.

(a) Name the purified form of the aluminium ore.

.............................................................. [1]

(b) Explain why the ore is mixed with cryolite.

.............................................................. [2]

(c) Explain why the mixture being electrolysed must be kept molten.

..............................................................

.............................................................. [2]

(d) At which electrode is the aluminium formed?

.............................................................. [1]

(e) Give the ionic equation for the formation of aluminium.

.............................................................. [2]

(f) Explain why the other electrode is replaced regularly.

..............................................................

.............................................................. [3]

(g) Give **two** uses of aluminium. State the property on which each use depends.

(i) Use ...................... Property ......................

(ii) Use ...................... Property ...................... [4]

**Total: 15 marks**
(NICCEA)

NOTE
*This question has a student answer with examiner's comments.* *See p. 96.*

### *Question 6 - Higher*

(a) The main ore of iron is haematite which is mainly iron (III) oxide. The ore is mixed with coke and limestone and added to a blast furnace to make iron.

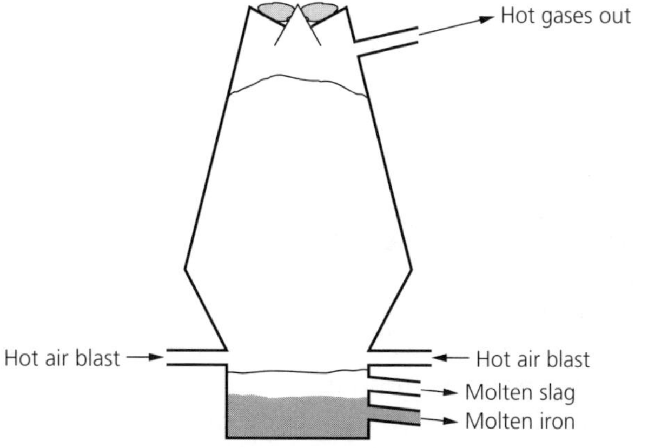


*Figure 4.7*

(i) What is meant by the term 'ore'?

. . . . . . . . . . . . . . . . . . . . . . . . . . . . . . . . . . . . . . . . . . . . . . . . . . . . . [1]

(ii) Name the **four** raw materials added to the blast furnace to produce iron.

. . . . . . . . . . . . . . . . . . . . . . . . . . . . . . . . . . . . . . . . . . . . . . . . . . . . . [2]

(b) The **two** reactions taking place which produce iron are:

iron (III) oxide + carbon → iron + carbon dioxide
iron (III) oxide + carbon monoxide → iron + carbon dioxide

(i) What type of reaction is the conversion of iron (III) oxide to iron?

. . . . . . . . . . . . . . . . . . . . . . . . . . . . . . . . . . . . . . . . . . . . . . . . . . . . . [1]

(ii) Explain the reason for your choice of reaction type in (b) (i).

. . . . . . . . . . . . . . . . . . . . . . . . . . . . . . . . . . . . . . . . . . . . . . . . . . . . . [1]

(iii) Why is limestone added to the mixture in the blast furnace?

. . . . . . . . . . . . . . . . . . . . . . . . . . . . . . . . . . . . . . . . . . . . . . . . . . . . . [1]

(c) The table below shows the properties of three steels.

| ***Steel*** | ***% carbon*** | ***Properties*** |
|---|---|---|
| Mild steel | 0.25 | Flexible (pliable) |
| Medium carbon steel | 0.40 | More springy, tougher |
| High carbon steel | 1.00 | Tough but brittle |

(i) Which steel would you use to make a saw blade?

. . . . . . . . . . . . . . . . . . . . . . . . . . . . . . . . . . . . . . . . . . . . . . . . . . . . . [1]

(ii) Explain the reason for your choice.

. . . . . . . . . . . . . . . . . . . . . . . . . . . . . . . . . . . . . . . . . . . . . . . . . . . . . [1]

# 5 Aqueous Chemistry – acids, bases and salts

## REVISION TIPS

- Make a table showing the names, formulae and acid-type (strong or weak) of the following acids: **sulphuric**, **hydrochloric**, **nitric** and **ethanoic (acetic)** acid.
- Make a table showing the names, formulae and alkali-type (strong or weak) of the following: **sodium hydroxide** (caustic soda), and **ammonia**.
- *Note*: It is a common error to believe that dilute acids and alkalis are the same as weak acids and alkalis.
- *Note*: That the **pH scale** is a measure of acidity or alkalinity and learn to recognise strong/weak acids/alkalis by the pH value of solutions of the same concentration.
- Learn the colours of the following indicators in acid, neutral and alkaline solution: **universal indicator**, **litmus**.
- The colours of universal indicator are the same as the rainbow colours: red (pH 1), orange (pH 3 ), yellow (pH 5), green (pH 7), blue (pH 9), indigo (pH 11), violet (pH 13).
- Learn that **neutralisation** of an acid by an alkali(base) produces a salt and water.
- Draw and label the apparatus to:
  - Prepare a soluble salt such as potassium chloride by titration.
  - Prepare a soluble salt, such as zinc sulphate, starting from its insoluble oxide or carbonate.
- Make a list of four of the most common salts and their everyday uses.
- Learn the tests for **anions** and **cations**.

## TOPIC OUTLINE

### Key definitions

- **Acids** are substances that:
  - turn universal indicator red /orange or blue litmus red;
  - neutralise alkalis/bases forming salts and water;
  - fizz with carbonates, e.g. marble chips, giving off **carbon dioxide** gas;
  - fizz with reactive metals, e.g. magnesium, giving off **hydrogen** gas;
  - when dissolved in water produce hydrogen ions, $\mathbf{H^+}$ (also shown as $\mathbf{H^+(aq)}$ (the hydrated hydrogen ion) and as $\mathbf{H_3O^+(aq)}$ (the hydroxonium ion) which are responsible for their acidic properties.
- **Bases** are substances that:
  - neutralise acids forming a salt and water;
  - are oxides or hydroxides of metals, e.g. CuO and KOH;
  - contain hydroxide ions, $\mathbf{OH^-}$, in aqueous solution.
- **Alkalis** are bases that are soluble in water, e.g. sodium hydroxide and ammonia solutions.

- A **salt** is the product of the neutralisation of an acid by a base/alkali, e.g.

  $HCl(aq) + NaOH(aq) \rightarrow NaCl\ (aq) + H_2O(l)$

  $NaCl(aq)$ is sodium chloride – 'common' salt.
- **Concentration of a solution** is usually given in moles/litre or as mol/dm$^3$. It is the number of moles of substance in 1 litre of solution.
- **Degree of dissociation of acids and alkalis** is the extent to which they react with water when in an aqueous solution. Complete dissociation produces 'strong' acids and alkalis; partial dissociation produces 'weak' acids and alkalis.

## Acids

- Many acids are **solutions** of oxides of non-metallic elements. For example:
  - Carbon dioxide solution is called carbonic acid ($H_2CO_3$).
  - Sulphur trioxide solution is called sulphuric acid ($H_2SO_4$).
- **Acid rain** is caused by the acidic oxides $SO_2$ and $NO_2$ dissolving in rain, e.g.

  $SO_2(g) + H_2O(aq) \rightarrow H_2SO_3(aq)$ (sulphurous acid)

> KEY POINT
> *Acids show their **acidity** only when dissolved in **water**, i.e. when they are aqueous. For example, HCl(aq) contains $H^+$(aq) but HCl(g) does not.*

- The **pH scale** of acids is shown in Figure 5.1.

*Figure 5.1*

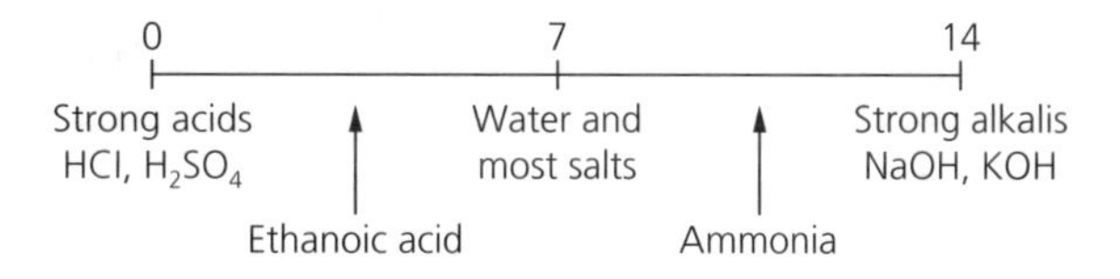


> HINT
> *Never use the word **strength** when you mean **concentration** – they are not interchangeable. Ethanoic acid becomes a stronger acid as its concentration decreases!*

### *Acid strength*

- The **strength** of an acid is related to the **concentration of hydrogen ions**, $H^+$, $H^+(aq)$ or $H_3O^+(aq)$, in the solution.
- The **concentration of hydrogen ions** in an acid solution is related to its degree of dissociation, or reaction with water (see definition above).
- **Strong acids** – an example is hydrochloric acid (HCl(aq)) which is a solution of hydrogen chloride in water:

$$HCl + H_2O \rightarrow H_3O^+ + Cl^-$$

hydrogen chloride + water → hydrated hydrogen ions + chloride ions

- The → indicates that the reaction goes to completion – 100 % of the HCl molecules are converted to hydrogen ions/ hydroxonium ions.
- **Weak acids** – an example is ethanoic acid/acetic acid ($CH_3CO_2H(aq)$):

  $$CH_3CO_2H + H_2O \rightleftarrows H_3O^+ + CH_3CO_2^-$$

- The $\rightleftarrows$ symbol indicates that the reaction does not go to completion, i.e. the reaction is only partial – in this case only about 1 % of the ethanoic acid molecules are converted into hydrogen ions/ hydroxonium ions.

## Alkalis and bases

All alkalis contain hydroxide ions ($OH^-$) in aqueous solution. Hydroxide ions neutralise the hydrogen ions in an acid. For example the reaction:

$NaOH(aq) + HCl(aq) \rightarrow NaCl(aq) + H_2O(l)$ is really

$OH^-(aq) + H^+(aq) \rightarrow H_2O(l)$

- An example of neutralisation by a base is:

$ZnO(s) + H_2SO_4(aq) \rightarrow ZnSO_4(aq) + H_2O(l)$

**or**

$ZnO(s) + 2H^+(aq) \rightarrow Zn^{2+}(aq) + H_2O(l)$

zinc oxide + sulphuric acid → zinc sulphate + water

- The common alkalis and bases used are shown in Figure 5.2.

*Figure 5.2* Common alkalis and bases

| ***Alkali/base*** | ***Formula*** | ***Salt produced/notes*** |
|---|---|---|
| Sodium hydroxide (caustic soda) | NaOH | Used to make sodium salts. |
| Calcium hydroxide | $Ca(OH)_2$ | In aqueous solution this is limewater. Used to test for $CO_2$. |
| Ammonia solution | $NH_3(aq)$ | Used to make ammonium salts. Also called ammonium hydroxide, $NH_4OH$. |
| Copper(II) oxide | CuO(s) | A base used to make copper salts, e.g. copper sulphate. |

- The common acids used are shown in Figure 5.3.

*Figure 5.3* Common acids

| ***Acid*** | ***Formula*** | ***Salt produced*** |
|---|---|---|
| Hydrochloric acid | HCl | Chlorides |
| Sulphuric acid | $H_2SO_4$ | Sulphates |
| Nitric acid | $HNO_3$ | Nitrates |
| Carbonic acid | $CO_2(aq)$ | Hydrogencarbonates/carbonates |

## Salts

HINT

*Before a salt can be prepared it is necessary to know whether it is **soluble** or **insoluble** in water. Methods of preparation differ for the two types.*

- Soluble salts include:
  - All nitrates, e.g. lead nitrate, silver nitrate.
  - All alkali metal salts, e.g. sodium chloride, potassium iodide.
  - All ammonium salts, e.g. ammonium nitrate, ammonium sulphate.
- Insoluble salts include:
  - Chlorides of silver and lead.
  - Sulphates of barium and calcium.

### *Preparation of salts*

- **Alkali metal salts** are prepared by **titration** to ensure the reaction of the exact quantities of chemicals required by the equation. For example,
- sodium chloride is formed by titration of equal numbers of moles of sodium hydroxide and hydrochloric acid using an acid/alkali indicator.

$NaOH(aq) + HCl(aq) \rightarrow NaCl(aq) + H_2O(l)$

- The **pure salt** is obtained by repeating the titration without indicator and crystallising the salt from a hot saturated solution of the product.
- **Soluble salts** may be prepared from an insoluble metal compound such as an oxide or a carbonate. The compound is added **in excess** to the acid. When all the acid has reacted, the **residue** of insoluble metal compound is filtered off. The pure salt is obtained by crystallisation, e.g.

$CuO(s) + H_2SO_4(aq) \rightarrow CuSO_4(aq) + H_2O(l)$

insoluble oxide → soluble salt

- **Insoluble salts** are prepared by **mixing** together solutions of reactants containing the **appropriate cation and anion**. They can be separated from the reaction mixture by filtration. For example, lead chloride forms from lead nitrate and sodium chloride solutions:

$Pb(NO_3)_2(aq) + 2NaCl(aq) \rightarrow PbCl_2(s) + 2NaNO_3(aq)$

## Testing for ions in solution

> HINT
> *Precipitation reactions are good examples of the reaction type called 'double decomposition'.*

### *Cation tests ($NH_4^+$ and metal ions)*

Metal cations can be recognised by a single test – the colour of the **precipitate** they form with **sodium hydroxide solution** OR the formation of ammonia gas. For example:

- $Al^{3+}$ and $Ca^{2+}$ – white
- $Cu^{2+}$ – pale blue
- $Fe^{2+}$ – dirty green BUT $Fe^{3+}$ – rusty brown
- $NH_4^+$ – gives no precipitate with sodium hydroxide but, on warming the mixture, **ammonia gas**, is produced which turns damp Universal Indicator paper blue.

> HINT
> *You can remember this by AA + AA → A. **A**ny **a**mmonium salt plus **a**ny **a**lkali gives **a**mmonia.*

### *Anion tests ( $OH^-$, $CO_3^{2-}$, $SO_4^{2-}$, halide ions and $NO_3^-$)*

The following test would be used in sequence on **different samples** of the same solution until a positive result is found.

1 Measure the pH of the solution. If it is 9 or more then hydroxide ions, $\mathbf{OH^-}$, will be present.
2 Add dilute nitric acid. If a gas is evolved which turns lime water milky then $\mathbf{CO_3^{2-}}$ ions are found.
3 Add silver nitrate solution *plus* dilute nitric acid. A precipitate forms with the three halide ions: $\mathbf{Cl^-}$ (white), $\mathbf{Br^-}$ (cream) and $\mathbf{I^-}$ (yellow).
4 Add barium chloride *plus* dilute hydrochloric acid. A white precipitate forms with the sulphate ion, $\mathbf{SO_4^{2-}}$.
5 Warm with sodium hydroxide solution mixed with aluminium powder. Ammonia is formed which turns damp Universal Indicator paper blue with $\mathbf{NO_3^-}$ ions.

> HINT
> *The acids used in tests 3 and 4 are not needed **if** carbonate **ions** are absent.*

## Uses of acids, alkalis and salts

### *Acids*

Acids common in everyday life include:

- **Vinegar** (acetic/ethanoic acid) – as a flavouring (condiment) and preservative (pickling). Also to neutralise wasp and sea urchin stings.
- **Citric acid** – the acid in lemon juice, sherbet and some 'Health Salts'.
- **Sulphuric acid** and **hydrochloric acids** – 'pickling' steel to remove rust before painting.
- **Tartaric acid** – in cake mixes with sodium bicarbonate to give the 'rise'.

> HINT
> *Remember **V** for **W**: **v**inegar (ethanoic acid) for **w**asps.*

### *Alkalis*

Alkalis common in everyday life include:

- **Lime** or **limestone** – used by farmers to correct soil pH (raise pH to 7) and in Scandinavia to neutralise acidity in lakes.
- **Sodium hydroxide solution** – oven cleaner, drain cleaner.
- **Ammonia solution** – to neutralise a bee sting or jellyfish sting.

> HINT
> *Remember **A** for **B** **a**mmonia for **b**ees.*

### *Salts*

Salts common in everyday life include:

- **Sodium chloride** – for preserving or flavouring food; de-icing roads.
- **Ammonium nitrate** – a nitrogenous fertiliser.
- **Silver bromide** – the light-sensitive chemical in photographic film.
- **Sodium hydrogencarbonate** – raising agent in cake mixes and as an indigestion cure.
- **Calcium carbonate** – in indigestion tablets.

## REVISION ACTIVITIES

**1** Fill in the missing words

(a) An acid is a substance that gives . . . . . . . . . . . . . . . . ions in aqueous solution.

(b) An alkali is a substance that gives . . . . . . . . . . . . . . . . ions in aqueous solution.

(c) An acid will . . . . . . . . . . . . . . . . an alkali to form a . . . . . . . . . . . . . . . .

and . . . . . . . . . . . . . . . . only.

(d) A weak acid is an acid that only . . . . . . . . . . . . . . . . dissociated in aqueous solution.

(e) An alkali is a . . . . . . . . . . . . . . . . base.

**2** Name:

(a) Three acids . . . . . . . . . . . . . . . . . . . . . . . . . . . . . . . . . . . . . . . . .

(b) Three alkalis . . . . . . . . . . . . . . . . . . . . . . . . . . . . . . . . . . . . . . . .

(c) Three insoluble bases . . . . . . . . . . . . . . . . . . . . . . . . . . . . . . . . . . .

**3** Choose one method from (a), (b) or (c) to make each of the salts (i), (ii), (iii).

(a) titration (b) base + acid (c) precipitation

(i) copper sulphate (ii) lead sulphate (iii) sodium sulphate?

**4** What will be the colour of Universal Indicator in each of the following:

(a) Sodium hydroxide solution (pH 13) . . . . . . . . . . . . . . . . . . . . . . . . . . . . . .

(b) Ammonia solution (pH 9) . . . . . . . . . . . . . . . . . . . . . . . . . . . . . . . . . . . .

(c) Ethanoic acid solution (pH 4) . . . . . . . . . . . . . . . . . . . . . . . . . . . . . . . .

**5** Write chemical equations to show how hydrogen ions are formed when the following substances react with water.

(a) Hydrogen chloride ($HCl$) . . . . . . . . . . . . . . . . . . . . . . . . . . . . . . . . . . .

(b) Ethanoic acid ($CH_3CO_2H$) . . . . . . . . . . . . . . . . . . . . . . . . . . . . . . . . .

**6** Label the following substances as acid(A), base(B), alkali (ALK) or salt (S).

- calcium carbonate ( )
- sodium hydroxide solution ( )
- copper (II) oxide ( )
- ammonia solution ( )

**7** What would be observed when sodium hydroxide solution is added to solutions of the following ions?

(a) calcium ions, $Ca^{2+}$ . . . . . . . . . . . . . . . . . . . . . . . . . . . . . . . . . . . . . .

(b) iron (II) ions, $Fe^{2+}$ . . . . . . . . . . . . . . . . . . . . . . . . . . . . . . . . . . . . .

(c) copper (II) ions, $Cu^{2+}$ . . . . . . . . . . . . . . . . . . . . . . . . . . . . . . . . . . .

**8** Label the following salts as soluble (S) or insoluble (IS):

- sodium chloride ( )
- ammonium sulphate ( )
- silver chloride ( )
- calcium nitrate ( )

**9** Give one common use for each of the following:

(a) ethanoic acid solution . . . . . . . . . . . . . . . . . . . . . . . . . . . . . . . . . . . . . . . . . .

(b) lime or slaked lime . . . . . . . . . . . . . . . . . . . . . . . . . . . . . . . . . . . . . . . . . . . .

(c) dilute sulphuric acid . . . . . . . . . . . . . . . . . . . . . . . . . . . . . . . . . . . . . . . . . . .

(d) sodium hydrogencarbonate . . . . . . . . . . . . . . . . . . . . . . . . . . . . . . . . . . . . . .

(e) ammonia solution . . . . . . . . . . . . . . . . . . . . . . . . . . . . . . . . . . . . . . . . . . . . .

## PRACTICE QUESTIONS

***Question 1 – Foundation***

Universal indicator changes colour at each pH. Universal indicator can be used to see if a solution is acidic, neutral or alkaline.

| | acidic | | | | | | | neutral | | | | alkaline | | | |
|---|---|---|---|---|---|---|---|---|---|---|---|---|---|---|---|
| pH | 0 | 1 | 2 | 3 | 4 | 5 | 6 | 7 | 8 | 9 | 10 | 11 | 12 | 13 | 14 |

(a) (i) Lemon juice has a pH of 3. What does this tell you about lemon juice?

. . . . . . . . . . . . . . . . . . . . . . . . . . . . . . . . . . . . . . . . . . . . . . . . . . [1]

(ii) What is the pH of pure water? . . . . . . . . . . . . . . . . . . . . . . . . . . . . . . [1]

(b) A sample of sulphuric acid has a pH of 2.

(i) Explain the difference between a dilute and a concentrated acid.

. . . . . . . . . . . . . . . . . . . . . . . . . . . . . . . . . . . . . . . . . . . . . . . . . . .

. . . . . . . . . . . . . . . . . . . . . . . . . . . . . . . . . . . . . . . . . . . . . . . . . . .

. . . . . . . . . . . . . . . . . . . . . . . . . . . . . . . . . . . . . . . . . . . . . . . . . . [2]

(ii) A neutral solution of universal indicator is green. When universal indicator is added to dilute acid, the solution goes red. How could you make the solution go green again?

. . . . . . . . . . . . . . . . . . . . . . . . . . . . . . . . . . . . . . . . . . . . . . . . . . .

. . . . . . . . . . . . . . . . . . . . . . . . . . . . . . . . . . . . . . . . . . . . . . . . . . .

. . . . . . . . . . . . . . . . . . . . . . . . . . . . . . . . . . . . . . . . . . . . . . . . . . [2]

(c) When copper carbonate is added to dilute sulphuric acid, carbon dioxide bubbles off (Figure 5.4).
The bubbles stop when the reaction is over (Figure 5.5).

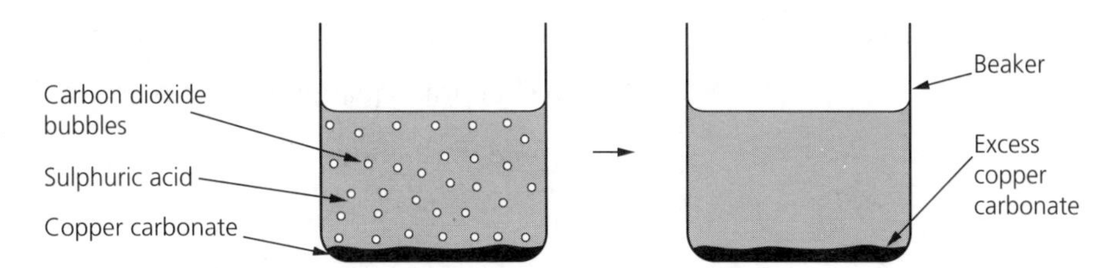


*Figures 5.4 and 5.5*

(i) Complete and label the diagram below to show how copper carbonate can be removed when the reaction is over.

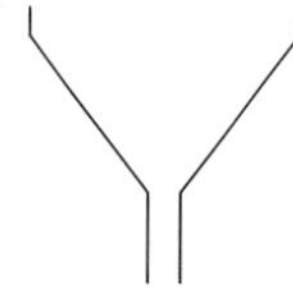

*Figure 5.6*

[3]

(ii) Give a simple test to show that the gas is carbon dioxide.

Test . . . . . . . . . . . . . . . . . . . . . . . . . . . . . . . . . . . . . . . . . . . . . . .

Result of test . . . . . . . . . . . . . . . . . . . . . . . . . . . . . . . . . . . . . . . . . . [2]

(iii) Complete the word equation for this reaction:

Copper carbonate + sulphuric acid → . . . . . . + . . . . . . + . . . . . . [3]

(iv) Name another compound that would react with sulphuric acid.

. . . . . . . . . . . . . . . . . . . . . . . . . . . . . . . . . . . . . . . . . . . . . . . . . . . [1]

**Total: 15 marks**
(SEG)

***Question 2 – Higher***

The salt sodium hydrogenphosphate ($Na_2HPO_4$), is used as a softening agent in processed cheese.

The salt can be made by reacting phosphoric acid, ($H_3PO_4$) with an alkali.

(a) Complete the name of an alkali that could react with phosphoric acid to make sodium hydrogenphosphate. . . . . . . . . . . . . . . . . . . . . . . . . . . . hydroxide [1]

(b) What name is given to a reaction in which an acid reacts with an alkali to make a salt? . . . . . . . . . . . . . . . . . . . . . . . . . . . . . . . . . . . . . . . . . . . . [1]

(c) Use the **Data Chapter** (on p. 119) to answer these questions.

(i) What colour is universal indicator in pure water . . . . . . . . . . . . . . . . . . [1]

(ii) A solution of phosphoric acid was tested with universal indicator solution. The indicator changed colour to orange. What was the pH of the phosphoric acid solution? . . . . . . . . . . . . . . . . . . . . . . . . . . . . . . . . . [1]

(d) How would the pH change when alkali is added to the phosphoric acid solution? . . . . . . . . . . . . . . . . . . . . . . . . . . . . . . . . . . . . . . . . . . . . . . . . . [1]

(e) (i) What ions are present when any acid is dissolved in water?

. . . . . . . . . . . . . . . . . . . . . . . . . . . . . . . . . . . . . . . . . . . . . . . . . . . [1]

(ii) What ions are present when any alkali is dissolved in water?

. . . . . . . . . . . . . . . . . . . . . . . . . . . . . . . . . . . . . . . . . . . . . . . . . . . [1]

(iii) Write a chemical equation for the reaction that takes place between the ions named in (i) and (ii) . . . . . . . . . . . . . . . . . . . . . . . . . . . . . . . . . [1]

**Total: 8 marks**
(NEAB)

### *Question 3 – Higher/Foundation*

**P**, **Q**, **R** and **S** are samples of water taken from different places thought to be polluted. The tables give the observations made when each sample of water was tested.

Figure 5.7

| *Test for sulphate ions* | *Observations* | | | |
|---|---|---|---|---|
| | *Sample P* | *Sample Q* | *Sample R* | *Sample S* |
| Add a few drops of dilute hydrochloric acid, then several drops of aqueous barium chloride. | A dense white precipitate was formed. | No change | A dense white precipitate was formed. | No change |

Figure 5.8

| *Test for chloride ions* | *Observations* | | | |
|---|---|---|---|---|
| | *Sample P* | *Sample Q* | *Sample R* | *Sample S* |
| Add a few drops of dilute nitric acid, then a few drops of aqueous silver nitrate. | No change | A faint white precipitate. | A dense white precipitate. | No change |

Use the results of the tests to help you answer the following questions.

(a) Which water sample is polluted with both sulphate ions and chloride ions?

. . . . . . . . . . . . . . . . . . . . . . . . . . . . . . . . . . . . . . . . . . . . . . [1]

(b) One of the samples was known to contain only ammonium sulphate. Which sample was this? . . . . . . . . . . . . . . . . . . . . . . . . . . . . . . . . . . [1]

(c) Give a reason for your answer to (b). . . . . . . . . . . . . . . . . . . . . . . . . .

. . . . . . . . . . . . . . . . . . . . . . . . . . . . . . . . . . . . . . . . . . . . . . [1]

(d) Which sample appears to be the least polluted? . . . . . . . . . . . . . . . . . . . [1]

**Total: 4 marks**
(MEG)

### *Question 4 – Foundation*

Compounds of sodium have important uses in industry and in the home. The following table (Figure 5.9) shows some of the properties of three sodium compounds.

Figure 5.9

| *Solution* | *Colour with universal indicator* | *pH* |
|---|---|---|
| Sodium carbonate | Blue | 9 |
| Sodium hydroxide | Purple/violet | 13 |
| Sodium chloride | Green | . . . . . . . . . . |

(a) Complete the table by putting in the pH of sodium chloride solution. [1]

(b) Which solution is neutral? . . . . . . . . . . . . . . . . . . . . . . . . . . . . . . . . [1]

(c) Which solution is the most alkaline? . . . . . . . . . . . . . . . . . . . . . . . . . . [1]

(d) Give **one** large-scale use of **two** of the sodium compounds listed in the table.

1. Sodium . . . . . . . . . . . . . . . . . . . . Use . . . . . . . . . . . . . . . . . . . . [1]

2. Sodium . . . . . . . . . . . . . . . . . . . . Use . . . . . . . . . . . . . . . . . . . . [1]

**Total: 5 marks**
(WJEC)

NOTE
*This question has a student answer with examiner's comments on p. 98.*

### *Question 5 - Higher*

The main acid in red and white wine is tartaric acid. It is usually present at a concentration of between 5 and 9 grams per litre, depending on the type of wine.

(a) Solutions of tartaric acid and sulphuric acid were compared. The solutions were of equal concentration. Some of the results are shown in the table.

*Figure 5.10*

| ***Test*** | ***Name of acid*** | |
|---|---|---|
| | ***Sulphuric acid*** | ***Tartaric acid*** |
| pH of solution. | 1 | 3.1 |
| Reaction with magnesium ribbon. | Fast reaction – vigorous bubbling. | Slow reaction – gentle bubbling. |
| Volume of sodium hydroxide solution required to neutralise 25 $cm^3$ of acid solution. | 25 $cm^3$ | 25 $cm^3$ |

The results of these tests suggest that one acid is strong and the other weak.

(i) Why are some acids said to be weak?

. . . . . . . . . . . . . . . . . . . . . . . . . . . . . . . . . . . . . . . . . . . . . . . .

. . . . . . . . . . . . . . . . . . . . . . . . . . . . . . . . . . . . . . . . . . . . . [2]

(ii) Name the weak acid and give a reason for your choice.

. . . . . . . . . . . . . . . . . . . . . . . . . . . . . . . . . . . . . . . . . . . . . . . .

. . . . . . . . . . . . . . . . . . . . . . . . . . . . . . . . . . . . . . . . . . . . . [1]

(b) (i) A titration can be used to find the volume of sodium hydroxide required to neutralise a volume of white wine. You are given some white wine, a solution of sodium hydroxide, phenophthalien and all necessary materials. Describe fully how you would carry out the titration.

. . . . . . . . . . . . . . . . . . . . . . . . . . . . . . . . . . . . . . . . . . . . . . . .

. . . . . . . . . . . . . . . . . . . . . . . . . . . . . . . . . . . . . . . . . . . . . . . .

. . . . . . . . . . . . . . . . . . . . . . . . . . . . . . . . . . . . . . . . . . . . . . . .

. . . . . . . . . . . . . . . . . . . . . . . . . . . . . . . . . . . . . . . . . . . . . . . .

. . . . . . . . . . . . . . . . . . . . . . . . . . . . . . . . . . . . . . . . . . . . . . . .

. . . . . . . . . . . . . . . . . . . . . . . . . . . . . . . . . . . . . . . . . . . . . [7]

(ii) Why would it be difficult to use this method for red wine?

. . . . . . . . . . . . . . . . . . . . . . . . . . . . . . . . . . . . . . . . . . . . . [1]

(c) In an experiment it was found that the acid present in 25 $cm^3$ of white wine was neutralised by 20 $cm^3$ of sodium hydroxide solution. The concentration of the sodium hydroxide solution was 0.10 moles per litre.

The reaction can be represented by the following equation in which tartarate is given the symbol T:

$H_2T = 2NaOH \rightarrow Na_2T + 2H_2O$

(i) Calculate the concentration in moles per litre of tartaric acid in the wine.

. . . . . . . . . . . . . . . . . . . . . . . . . . . . . . . . . . . . . . . . . . . . . . . .

. . . . . . . . . . . . . . . . . . . . . . . . . . . . . . . . . . . . . . . . . . . . . . . .

. . . . . . . . . . . . . . . . . . . . . . . . . . . . . . . . . . . . . . . . . . . . . [3]

(ii) Suggest why the concentration of tartaric acid in the wine may be less than that found by titration. . . . . . . . . . . . . . . . . . . . . . . . . . . . . . . . [1]

**Total: 15 marks**

(NEAB)

# 6 How far, how fast and energetics

## REVISION TIPS

- Note that *all* reactions are reversible, but some are very difficult to reverse.
- Reversible reactions are represented by the $\rightleftarrows$ sign and when equilibrium has been reached in a reversible reaction the $\leftrightharpoons$ sign is used.
- Make sure that you understand the difference between a **reversible reaction** and when **equilibrium** has been reached.
- Learn Le Chatelier's principle, from this you will be able to predict (and get right!) the conditions for various industrial processes that involve establishing an equilibrium to maximise the product including the Haber process and the Contact process.
- The factors that affect the equilibrium can be remembered by **TCP** – **T**emperature, **C**oncentration and **P**ressure.
- If you need to name a catalyst remember that transition metals and their compounds are all good catalysts.
- Learn the conditions that affect the rate (speed) of reactions and the experiments that are used to measure rate of reactions. Try to think of a mnemonic such as **St CC** (Saint CC) – **S**ize; **T**emperature, **C**atalyst, **C**oncentration.
- You can remember that exothermic reactions **give out** heat by thinking of the word **exit**.
- Note that all combustion reactions are exothermic.
- You should try to understand why chemical reactions occur – the chemicals must have **AC**, i.e. an amount of energy called the **A**ctivation energy and that the particles must **C**ollide.

## TOPIC OUTLINE

### Key definitions

- A **reversible reaction** is a reaction that can be reversed by changing the conditions.
- **Thermal dissociation** occurs when a chemical is broken down by the action of heat and the products recombine on cooling to re-form the original substance. The action of heat on ammonium chloride to form ammonia and hydrogen chloride is an example of a reversible reaction (and thermal dissociation):

  $NH_4Cl(s) \rightleftarrows NH_3(g) + HCl(g)$

- A reaction is said to be in **dynamic equilibrium** when the rate of the forward reaction equals the rate of the reverse reaction. For example, $N_2(g) + 3H_2(g) \leftrightharpoons 2NH_3(g)$ would be in dynamic equilibrium when the rate of nitrogen gas reacting with hydrogen gas is equal to the rate of decomposition of ammonia.

- **Le Chatelier's principle** states that, 'If an equilibrium is disturbed by changing the conditions such as temperature, pressure or concentration, the equilibrium will alter to oppose the change, and a new equilibrium will be established.'
- A **catalyst** increases the rate of a reaction, but it is not used up in the reaction. A catalyst reaction will have a lower activation energy than the uncatalysed reaction.

> HINT
> *Note that a catalyst may take part in the reaction but it is NOT used up.*

- **Enzymes** are biological catalysts produced within living organisms. They are used in the manufacture of a wide variety of materials including alcohol, bread and yoghurt.
- An **exothermic** reaction is a reaction that gives out energy.
- An **endothermic** reaction is a reaction that takes in energy.
- **Activation energy** is the minimum total energy that colliding particles require before they can react.

## How far - equilibrium

- Some reactions can go both ways (**reversible**). For example, when **hydrated** copper sulphate crystals are heated they lose water:

  $CuSO_4.5H_2O(s) \rightarrow CuSO_4(s) + 5H_2O(g)$

  But when water is added to **anhydrous** copper sulphate, hydrated copper sulphate is formed:

  $CuSO_4(s) + 5H_2O(g) \rightarrow CuSO_4.5H_2O(s)$

  The reaction can be summarised using the $\rightleftarrows$ sign:

  $CuSO_4.5H_2O(s) \rightleftarrows CuSO_4(s) + 5H_2O(g)$

- Indicators are examples of a **dynamic equilibrium**, e.g. methyl orange which we will represent by HX . HX is a weak acid and ionises into $H^+$ ions and $X^-$ ions. HX is red whereas the $X^-$ ion is yellow. In water the following equilibrium occurs:

  $HX(aq) \rightleftharpoons H^+(aq) + X^-(aq)$
  red yellow

> HINT
> *$\rightleftarrows$ is the sign for a reversible reaction and $\rightleftharpoons$ means that the reaction is in equilibrium.*

- By **Le Chatelier's principle**:
  - when an **acid** is added ($H^+$ ions), the equilibrium position will move to the left to remove the $H^+$ ions; HX molecules will be formed (and $X^-(aq)$ will be removed) and the solution will go red.
  - When an **alkali** is added ($OH^-$ ions), it will remove the $H^+$ ions to form water; the equilibrium position will shift to the right to form more $H^+$ ions and more $X^-$ ions so the solution will go yellow.
  - When there are an equal number of HX molecules and $X^-$ ions, the solution will be orange.

> KEY POINT
> *Make sure you understand the above, and how Le Chatelier's principle is used to predict the condition.*

- The reaction $N_2(g) + 3H_2(g) \rightleftharpoons 2NH_3(g)$ is exothermic.
  You should be able to predict that this reaction will require a high pressure and a low temperature. Since lowering the temperature slows down reactions, a catalyst will be required to speed up the reaction. In this case the catalyst is iron.

## How fast – rate (or speed) of reactions

KEY POINT

*The rate of reaction can be measured noting the time it takes for a certain amount of reaction to occur.*

The commonest methods of measuring reactions are:

HINT

*When you are asked to describe a rate experiment, if there is a **loss in mass** use method 1, if a **gas is given off** use method 2.*

1 Measuring the change in mass at fixed intervals of times. In the reaction between calcium carbonate (marble chips) and hydrochloric acid, measure the loss in mass as carbon dioxide is given off at 30-second intervals. See Figure 6.1 shows the set-up before the reactants are mixed.

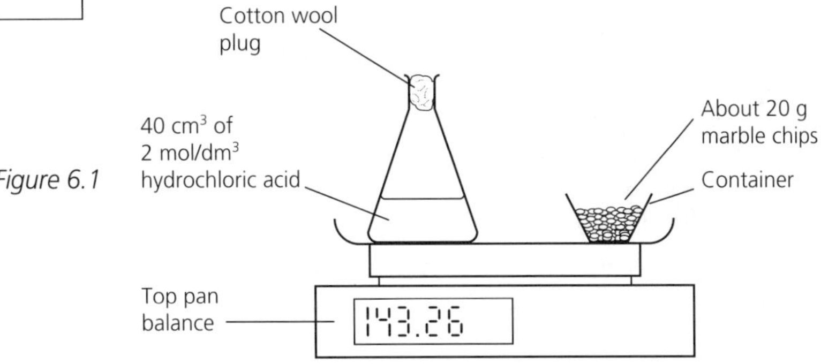

*Figure 6.1*

2 Measuring the change in volume at fixed intervals of time. In the decomposition of hydrogen peroxide, measure the volume of oxygen given off at 30-second intervals. See Figure 6.2.

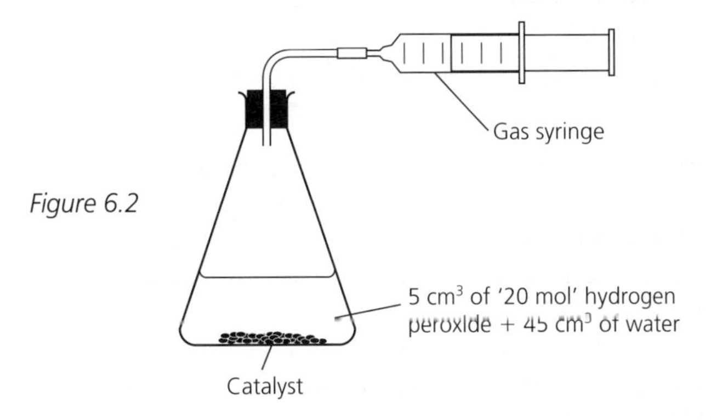

*Figure 6.2*

3 Noting the time it takes for a substance to react completely. In the reaction between magnesium and hydrochloric acid, measure the time it takes for the magnesium to react completely. See Figure 6.3.

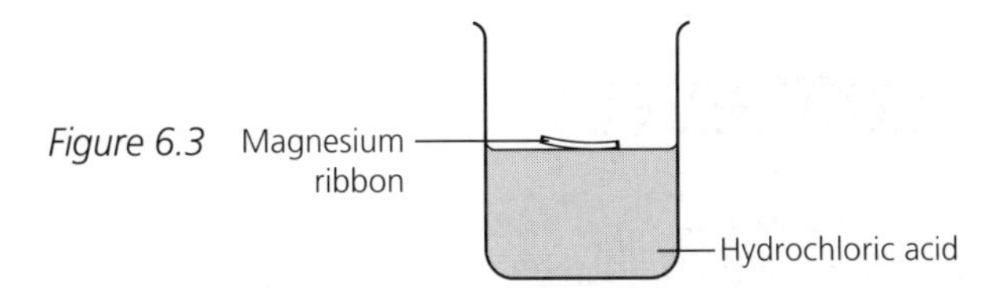

*Figure 6.3*

4 Noting the time it takes for a product to form. In the reaction between sodium thiosulphate and hydrochloric acid, noting the time it takes for the sulphur to form. See Figure 6.4.

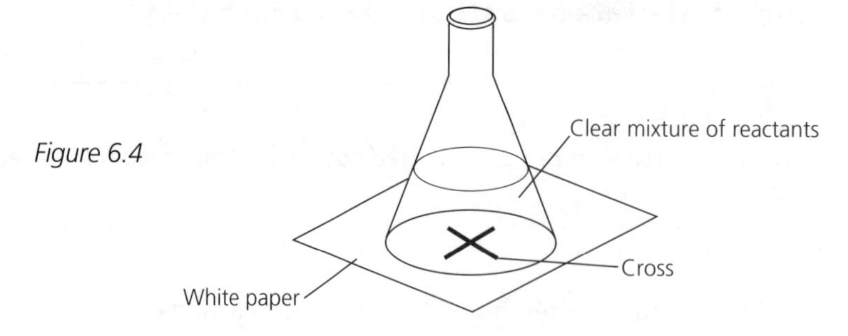


*Figure 6.4*

- Plot the change measured against time on a graph. The slope of the graph will give the rate of reaction – the steeper the slope the faster the rate of reaction. In the graph (Figure 6.5) it can be seen that the reaction was faster at the start of the reaction, and got slower as the reactants were used up.

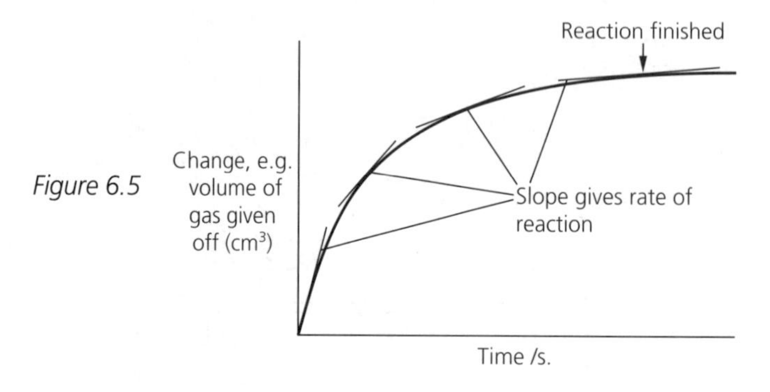


*Figure 6.5*

HINT
*All combustion reactions are exothermic.*

- Most reactions give out energy – they are **exothermic**.
- A few reactions take in energy – they are **endothermic**. Photosynthesis is an example of an endothermic reaction.

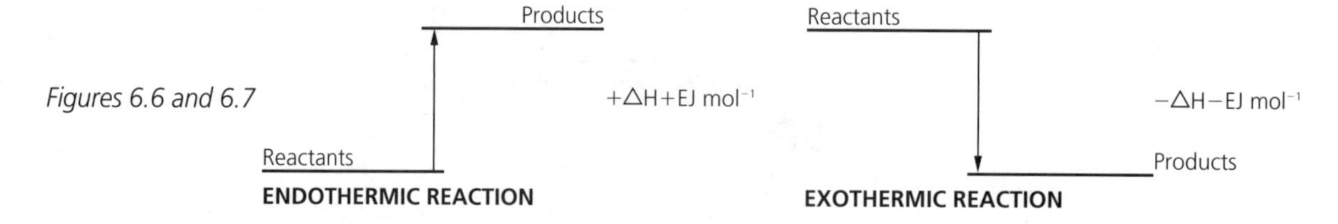


*Figures 6.6 and 6.7*

- In an **exothermic reaction**, the reactants have more energy than the products formed. In an **endothermic reaction**, the products have more energy than the reactants.
- In order for chemicals to react they must collide *and* have energy sufficient for them to react. This is called the **activation energy**.
- You should be able to see why increasing the temperature and increasing the surface area of chemicals speeds up the rate of reactions, for in each case the number of collisions is increased. Raising the temperature also increases the number of particles with energy greater than the activation energy.

## REVISION ACTIVITIES

1 Fill in the missing word.

(a) When the rate of the forward reaction equals the rate of the reverse reaction, the reaction is said to be in . . . . . . . . . . . . . . . . .

(b) A substance that speeds up a chemical reaction, but is not used up in the reaction is called a . . . . . . . . . . . . . . . . .

(c) . . . . . . . . . . . . . . . . are biological catalysts.

(d) Reactions that give out heat energy are called . . . . . . . . . . . . . . . . reactions.

(e) The presence of . . . . . . . . . . . . . . . . can be tested by adding anhydrous copper(II) sulphate, the colour change is from white to blue.

**2** The apparatus used in the diagram below was used to study how the rate of reaction of hydrogen peroxide was effected by using various catalysts.

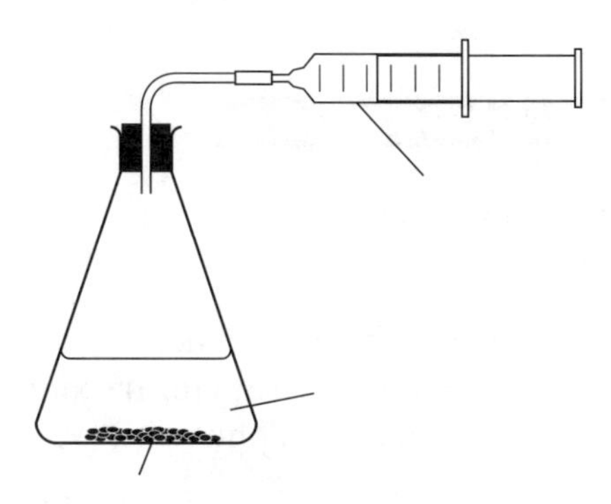

*Figure 6.8*

(a) Label the diagram clearly.

(b) Suggest three different catalysts that you could use for this experiment.

. . . . . . . . . . . . . . . . . . . . . . . . . . . . . . . . . . . . . . . . . . . . . . . . . . . .

(c) Write the equation for the decomposition of hydrogen peroxide into water and oxygen. . . . . . . . . . . . . . . . . . . . . . . . . . . . . . . . . . . . . . .

(d) What is the test to show the presence of water? . . . . . . . . . . . . . . . . . . . . . .

(e) What is the test for oxygen gas? . . . . . . . . . . . . . . . . . . . . . . . . . . . . . . . .

The sketch shows the total volume of oxygen collected measured against time.

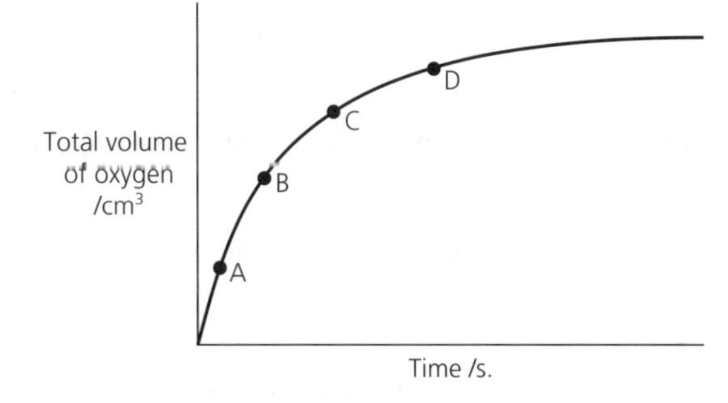


*Figure 6.9*

(f) At which point A, B, C or D, is the rate of reaction fastest? . . . . . . . . . . . . .

(g) Why does the graph become horizontal? . . . . . . . . . . . . . . . . . . . . . . . . . . .

(h) Suggest two other ways (other than using a catalyst) that would speed up this reaction. . . . . . . . . . . . . . . . . . . . . . . . . . . . . . . . . . . . . . . . . . .

. . . . . . . . . . . . . . . . . . . . . . . . . . . . . . . . . . . . . . . . . . . . . . . . . . . .

**3** When hydrogen reacts with oxygen to form water, energy is released.

(a) (i) Write the symbol equation for this reaction, including state symbols.

. . . . . . . . . . . . . . . . . . . . . . . . . . . . . . . . . . . . . . . . . . . . . . . . . . .

In this reaction the bonds in hydrogen molecules and oxygen molecules are broken.

(ii) Is bond breaking an endothermic or exothermic process? . . . . . . . . . .

(iii) What bonds are formed in this reaction? . . . . . . . . . . . . . . . . . . . . . . . .

(b) State three different forms in which energy may be released in this reaction. . . . . . . . . . . . . . . . . . . . . . . . . . . . . . . . . . . . . . . . . . . . . . . . . . .

## PRACTICE QUESTIONS

***Question 1 – Foundation***

The main steps in the manufacture of sulphuric acid are:

**1** sulphur + oxygen → sulphur dioxide
**2** sulphur dioxide + oxygen ⇄ sulphur trioxide
**3** sulphur trioxide + water → sulphuric acid

(a) In Step 2 the gases are heated to 400–500 °C and passed over an oxide of vanadium. Why are these conditions used?

. . . . . . . . . . . . . . . . . . . . . . . . . . . . . . . . . . . . . . . . . . . . . . . . . . . . . . .

. . . . . . . . . . . . . . . . . . . . . . . . . . . . . . . . . . . . . . . . . . . . . . . . . . . . . . .

. . . . . . . . . . . . . . . . . . . . . . . . . . . . . . . . . . . . . . . . . . . . . . . . . . . . . . . [2]

(b) Steps 1 and 3 are highly exothermic. Explain how this effects the economic efficiency of the manufacturing process.

. . . . . . . . . . . . . . . . . . . . . . . . . . . . . . . . . . . . . . . . . . . . . . . . . . . . . . .

. . . . . . . . . . . . . . . . . . . . . . . . . . . . . . . . . . . . . . . . . . . . . . . . . . . . . . . [2]

**Total: 4 marks**
(WJEC part question)

***Question 2 – Higher***

A student placed some marble chips in some dilute hydrochloric acid and a gas was produced.

$CaCO_3(s) + 2HCl(aq) \rightarrow CaCl_2(aq) + H_2O(l) + CO_2(g)$

(a) Give the name of the gas produced. . . . . . . . . . . . . . . . . . . . . . . . . . . . . . . [1]

(b) The student repeated the experiment with a small cube of marble (excess) and 25 cm$^3$ of the acid and measured the volume of gas evolved at 10 second intervals.

This table of results was obtained.

| ***Time (s)*** | 0 | 10 | 20 | 30 | 40 | 50 | 60 |
|---|---|---|---|---|---|---|---|
| ***Volume (cm$^3$)*** | 0 | 20 | 30 | 36 | 39 | 40 | 40 |

(i) [On a separate sheet of graph paper] draw a graph of these results. Plot the time on the horizontal ($x$) axis. Use the graph, where necessary, to answer the questions which follow.

(ii) After how many seconds did the reaction stop? . . . . . . . . . . . . . . . . . . . .

(iii) From what simple observation would the student know that the reaction had stopped? ....................................................

(iv) What would the student SEE which shows that all the acid, rather that all of the marble, had been used by the end of the reaction?

....................................................

(v) What volume of gas had been collected at the end of the experiment?

.................................................... [8]

(c) The experiment was repeated with THREE pieces of marble, each of the same size as before, and 25 $cm^3$ of the same acid.

(i) At the start of the experiment, would the gas be produced more quickly, less quickly or at the same rate as in the first experiment?

....................................................

(ii) Give a reason for your answer to (i). ....................................................

....................................................

(iii) Sketch, on the grid, using a **broken** line (- - - - -) the sort of curve which might have been produced in this experiment. [4]

**Total: 13 marks**
(London)

***Question 3 – Higher***

Hydrogen peroxide decomposes very slowly at room temperature.

hydrogen peroxide → water + oxygen

Adding manganese dioxide speeds up this reaction without altering the products.

A student investigated this reaction by adding 1 g of manganese dioxide to 50 $cm^3$ of hydrogen peroxide. The student measured the volume of oxygen produced during five minutes. The results are shown in the table.

| *Time (minutes)* | 0 | 1 | 2 | 3 | 4 | 5 |
|---|---|---|---|---|---|---|
| *Total volume of oxygen given off ($cm^3$)* | 0 | 27 | 41 | 48 | 50 | 50 |

(a) Draw a graph of these results on a separate sheet of graph paper. Join the points with a smooth curve. Label your curve 'X' [4]

(b) The student repeated the experiment. This time the student added 1 g of manganese dioxide to a mixture of 25 $cm^3$ of hydrogen peroxide and 25 $cm^3$ of water.

**On the graph**, sketch the curve you would expect if all the other conditions remained the same as in the first experiment. [2]

(c) Explain, in terms of particles, why the rate of reaction slows down during the experiment. ....................................................

....................................................

.................................................... [3]

(d) Explain, in terms of particles, why increasing the temperature may increase the rate of a chemical reaction. ....................................................

....................................................

.................................................... [3]

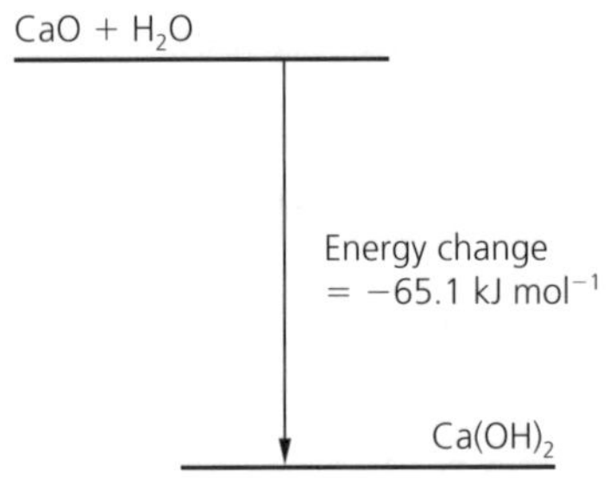

$CaO + H_2O$

Energy change $= -65.1 \text{ kJ mol}^{-1}$

$Ca(OH)_2$

*Figure 6.12*

(e) In a reaction known as 'slaking', water is added to calcium oxide to produce calcium hydroxide. The calcium hydroxide is then used to make plaster.

$CaO + H_2O \rightarrow Ca(OH)_2$

The diagram represents the energy change during this reaction.

(i) What does the diagram tell us about the energy change which takes place in this reaction?

. . . . . . . . . . . . . . . . . . . . . . . . . . . . . . . . . . . . . . . . . . . . . . . .

. . . . . . . . . . . . . . . . . . . . . . . . . . . . . . . . . . . . . . . . . . . . . . . . [2]

(ii) What does the diagram indicate about the relative amount of energy required to break bonds and form new bonds in this reaction?

. . . . . . . . . . . . . . . . . . . . . . . . . . . . . . . . . . . . . . . . . . . . . . . .

. . . . . . . . . . . . . . . . . . . . . . . . . . . . . . . . . . . . . . . . . . . . . . . .

. . . . . . . . . . . . . . . . . . . . . . . . . . . . . . . . . . . . . . . . . . . . . . . .

. . . . . . . . . . . . . . . . . . . . . . . . . . . . . . . . . . . . . . . . . . . . . . . . [3]

**Total: 17 marks**
(NEAB)

NOTE
*This question has a student answer with examiner's comments on* *p. 99.*

***Question 4 – Higher***

Ammonia, $NH_3$, is made by reacting together hydrogen and nitrogen in the presence of iron. This reaction is called the Haber process.

(a) How does the presence of iron help the process?

. . . . . . . . . . . . . . . . . . . . . . . . . . . . . . . . . . . . . . . . . . . . . . . . . . . [1]

(b) The table shows how much ammonia is produced using different conditions.

| | ***Percentage yield of ammonia at these temperatures*** | | |
|---|---|---|---|
| ***Pressure/atm*** | 100 °C | 300 °C | 500 °C |
| 25 | 91.7 | 27.4 | 2.9 |
| 50 | 94.5 | 39.5 | 5.6 |
| 100 | 96.7 | 52.5 | 10.6 |
| 200 | 98.4 | 66.7 | 18.3 |
| 400 | 99.4 | 79.7 | 31.9 |

From the values in the table, what happens to the yield of ammonia as:

(i) The temperature is increased? . . . . . . . . . . . . . . . . . . . . . . . . . . . . . . . [1]

(ii) The pressure is increased? . . . . . . . . . . . . . . . . . . . . . . . . . . . . . . . . . [1]

(c) Using ideas about particles colliding, explain how the rate of reaction will change as the temperature increases. . . . . . . . . . . . . . . . . . . . . . . . . . . . . . . .

. . . . . . . . . . . . . . . . . . . . . . . . . . . . . . . . . . . . . . . . . . . . . . . . . . . [3]

(d) The Haber process is usually carried out at a higher temperature than the one which would give the highest yield. Suggest a reason for this.

. . . . . . . . . . . . . . . . . . . . . . . . . . . . . . . . . . . . . . . . . . . . . . . . . . . [1]

**Total: 7 marks**
(MEG)

# 7 Metals, non-metals and compounds

## REVISION TIPS

- Metals ending in **-ium** are manufactured by electrolysis, e.g. sodium, potassium, calcium and aluminium. They tend to be very reactive.
- Other metals such as iron, silver, gold and lead either occur in the free state or their metal oxides are easily reduced. They tend to be unreactive.
- The non-metals that are gases end in either **-ine**, e.g. chlorine and bromine, or **-gen**, e.g. oxygen and nitrogen, or **-on**, e.g. the inert gases argon and neon (carbon is an exception to this rule). Sulphur and phosphorus are also non-metals.
- If you divide the Periodic Table diagonally from top left to bottom right, the metals are to the **left** of the line and non-metals to the **right**.
- Compounds of two elements have **-ide** endings. The compound between magnesium and oxygen is magnesium oxide; and the compound between sodium and chlorine is sodium chloride.
- Compounds containing oxygen have **-ate** endings, e.g. copper sulphate, lead nitrate and calcium carbonate.
- Learn the **order of reactivity** of metals and non-metals – Group 1 metals are the most reactive and transition metals the least reactive.
- Make a table to show the difference in **physical** properties and **chemical** properties of metals and non-metals.
- Learn the conditions for **rusting** and the way rusting can be prevented.
- Make a list of the **uses** of metals, non-metals and their compounds.
- Remember that carbon and sulphur form **allotropes**. Learn the names and properties of these allotropes plus the structures of the allotropes of carbon.

## TOPIC OUTLINE

### Key definitions

- A **metal** is an element which forms positive ions by the loss of electrons.
- A **non-metal** is an element which forms negative ions by the gain of electrons.
- **Allotropy** is the existence of more than one form of an element in the same physical state.
- The **reactivity series** (reactivity table) of metallic elements is a list or table in which the most reactive metal is placed at the top of the series and the least reactive metal is placed at the bottom.
- Metals **corrode** because they react with oxygen to give oxides.

## Differences between metals and non-metals

You should make sure that you know the **physical** and **chemical** differences between metals and non-metals.

### *Physical differences*

| *Metal* | *Non-metal* |
|---|---|
| Malleable (can be bent) | Brittle when solid (break easily) |
| Good conductors of heat and electricity | Poor conductors of heat and electricity (insulators) |
| Have high melting points and boiling points (except the alkali metals) | Have low melting points and boiling points (except carbon and silicon) |
| Have high densities (except the alkali metals) | Have low densities |

### *Chemical differences*

| *Metal* | *Non-metal* |
|---|---|
| Form basic oxides | Form acidic oxides |
| Their chlorides are ionic, e.g. $Na^+Cl^-$ | Their chlorides are covalent e.g. HCl |
| They are reducing agents (tend to lose electrons), | They are oxidising agents (tend to gain electrons), |
| e.g. $Na \rightarrow Na^+ + e^-$ | e.g. $Cl_2 + 2e^- \rightarrow 2Cl^-$ |
| React with acids to give hydrogen, | Do not react with acids |
| e.g. $Mg(s) + 2HCl(aq) \rightarrow MgCl_2(aq) + H_2(g)$ | |

## Reactivity series for metals

KEY POINT

*The reactivity series of metals is a list with the most reactive metal at the top of the series and the least reactive at the bottom.*

<table>
<tr><th>Metal</th><th>Reaction with oxygen</th><th>Reaction with water</th><th>Reaction with dilute hydrochloric acid</th></tr>
<tr><td>Sodium</td><td rowspan="5">All react to give oxide when heated – the reactions become less vigorous as you go down from sodium to copper</td><td>Reacts with cold water</td><td>Reacts explosively</td></tr>
<tr><td>Magnesium</td><td rowspan="2">React with steam</td><td rowspan="3">React forming metal chloride and hydrogen</td></tr>
<tr><td>Iron</td></tr>
<tr><td>Lead</td><td rowspan="2">No reaction</td></tr>
<tr><td>Copper</td><td>No reaction</td></tr>
</table>

- In general a more reactive metal can displace a less reactive metal from a solution of one of its salts.

| | *Magnesium sulphate* | *Iron sulphate* | *Lead nitrate* | *Copper sulphate* |
|---|---|---|---|---|
| **Magnesium** | | Iron formed, solution turns from green to colourless | Lead formed, no colour change | Copper formed, solution changes from blue to colourless |
| **Iron** | No reaction | | Lead formed, solution changes from colourless to green | Copper deposited, solution changes from blue to green |
| **Lead** | No reaction | No reaction | | Copper deposited, solution changes from blue to colourless |
| **Copper** | No reaction | No reaction | No reaction | |

- Magnesium displaces zinc from zinc sulphate and zinc displaces iron from iron sulphate. This tells you that zinc is less reactive than magnesium but more reactive than iron. You would predict that zinc would react with steam and with hydrochloric acid to give hydrogen.

## Corrosion

- **Corrosion** refers to the gradual action of air and water on metals.
- When aluminium corrodes it forms a protective layer of aluminium oxide. Lead and copper behave in a similar way.
- Copper oxide reacts further with carbonic acid (carbon dioxide dissolved in water) to form a green, basic carbonate of copper often seen on a copper roof.
- Silver, platinum and gold do *not* corrode (although silver reacts with hydrogen sulphide to form black silver sulphide – you may have seen this if you have put peas in a silver container or a silver spoon into an egg or a silver fork into meat).
- **Rusting** is a special case of corrosion.

### *Rusting*

HINT
*Iron is the only metal that is said to rust when it corrodes.*

- For rusting to take place both **oxygen** and **air** must be present.
- Rusting can be prevented by stopping iron from coming into contact with water or air, e.g. by painting or greasing iron or coating with a metal such as chromium.

## Reactivity series for non-metals

KEY POINT
*Reactive non-metals displace less reactive metals from solutions of their salts.*

| | *Sodium chloride* | *Water (hydrogen oxide)* | *Sodium bromide* | *Sodium iodide* |
|---|---|---|---|---|
| ***Chlorine*** | | Oxygen formed | Bromine formed | Iodine formed |
| ***Oxygen*** | No reaction | | Bromine formed | Iodine formed |
| ***Bromine*** | No reaction | No reaction | | Iodine formed |
| ***Iodine*** | No reaction | No reaction | No reaction | |

► Iodine displaces sulphur from sodium sulphide solution, hence sulphur must be less reactive than iodine. You would predict that if chlorine were bubbled into sodium sulphide solution, sulphur would be deposited. You would also predict that the reaction of chlorine with iron would be more rapid than the reaction of iodine with iron.

### *Noble gases*

The **noble gases** (or inert gases) such as helium, neon and argon are almost totally unreactive.

HINT
*Noble gases are used when an unreactive atmosphere is required such as in electric light bulbs.*

## Some uses of non-metals, metals and compounds

| *Metal* | *Use* | *Non-metal* | *Use* | *Compound* | *Use* |
|---|---|---|---|---|---|
| **Aluminium** | Cooking utensils | **Chlorine** | Sterilising water | **Sodium chloride** | Food industry |
| **Iron** | Manufacture of steels | **Argon** | Lighting | **Ammonia** | Manufacture of fertilisers |
| **Copper** | Electrical wires | **Carbon** | Electrodes | **Calcium oxide** | Neutralise soil |
| **Tin** | Coating steel cans | **Oxygen** | Steel making | **Calcium carbonate** | Manufacture of concrete |
| **Lead** | Car batteries | **Helium** | Filling balloons | **Sodium hydroxide** | Manufacture of soap |
| **Zinc** | Galvanising steels | **Iodine** | Making antiseptics | **Sulphuric acid** | Car batteries |

## REVISION ACTIVITIES

**1** Fill in the missing word.

(a) Metals are . . . . . . . . . . . . . . . . . (they can be easily bent).

(b) Metal oxides are . . . . . . . . . . . . . . . . . .

(c) Metals react with dilute acids to give . . . . . . . . . . . . . . . . . gas.

(d) The oxides of . . . . . . . . . . . . . . . . . are acidic.

(e) The . . . . . . . . . . . . . . . . . gases are unreactive.

(f) Graphite and diamond are . . . . . . . . . . . . . . . . . of carbon.

**2** Using only the metals in the list below, answer the questions that follow:

calcium copper lead potassium zinc

(a) Arrange the metals in order of decreasing reactivity, putting the most reactive metal first. . . . . . . . . . . . . . . . . . . . . . . . . . . . . . . . . . . . . . . . . .

(b) Which of these metals are manufactured by electrolysis?

. . . . . . . . . . . . . . . . . . . . . . . . . . . . . . . . . . . . . . . . . . . . . . . . . .

(c) Which metal is used in household electrical wiring systems?

. . . . . . . . . . . . . . . . . . . . . . . . . . . . . . . . . . . . . . . . . . . . . . . . . .

(d) Describe what you would see if you placed excess zinc metal into copper sulphate solution. . . . . . . . . . . . . . . . . . . . . . . . . . . . . . . . . . . . . . . . . .

(e) Which one of the above metals forms a soluble carbonate?

. . . . . . . . . . . . . . . . . . . . . . . . . . . . . . . . . . . . . . . . . . . . . . . . . . . .

(f) Which one of the above metals forms positive ions most readily?

. . . . . . . . . . . . . . . . . . . . . . . . . . . . . . . . . . . . . . . . . . . . . . . . . . . .

**3** Using only the non-metals in the list below answer the questions that follow:

bromine chlorine fluorine iodine oxygen sulphur

(a) Arrange the non-metals in order of reactivity, placing the most reactive non-metal first. . . . . . . . . . . . . . . . . . . . . . . . . . . . . . . . . . . . . . . .

(b) Which one of these non-metals is used to test to see if an organic compounds is unsaturated? . . . . . . . . . . . . . . . . . . . . . . . . . . . . . . . . .

(c) Which non-metals form ions with a charge of $2^-$? . . . . . . . . . . . . . . . . . . . .

(d) Which non-metal is used in the manufacture of steel? . . . . . . . . . . . . . . . .

(e) Which non-metal is used for vulcanising rubber? . . . . . . . . . . . . . . . . . . . . .

(f) Which of these non-metals is a liquid at room temperature? . . . . . . . . . . .

**4** Give examples of the following types of reactions:

**(a) Synthesis** involving a metal and a non-metal. . . . . . . . . . . . . . . . . . . . . . . . .

(b) **Oxidation** of a non-metal to form a gas. . . . . . . . . . . . . . . . . . . . . . . . . . . .

(c) **Displacement** of one metal by another metal. . . . . . . . . . . . . . . . . . . . . . . .

(d) Hydrogen **reducing** a non-metal. . . . . . . . . . . . . . . . . . . . . . . . . . . . . . . .

(e) Two non-metals taking part in a **reversible** reaction. . . . . . . . . . . . . . . . . .

. . . . . . . . . . . . . . . . . . . . . . . . . . . . . . . . . . . . . . . . . . . . . . . . . . . .

## PRACTICE QUESTIONS

### *Question 1 – Foundation*

The figure below shows a series of experiments set up to investigate the rusting of iron.

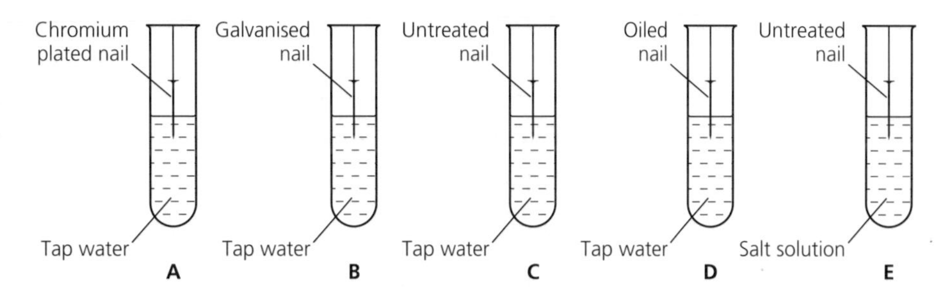


*Figure 7.1*

(a) In which **two** experiments would rusting take place after a short time?

. . . . . . . . . . . . . . . . . . . . . . . . . . . **and** . . . . . . . . . . . . . . . . . . . . . . . . . . . [2]

(b) In which experiment would rusting take place most quickly?

. . . . . . . . . . . . . . . . . . . . . . . . . . . . . . . . . . . . . . . . . . . . . . . . . . . . [1]

(c) In which experiment had the nails received a treatment which could be used on bicycle handlebars? ..........................................

metal dustbins .................................................. [2]

(d) What process could be used to obtain salt from the solution in E?

.................................................. [1]

**Total: 6 marks**
(MEG)

***Question 2 – Higher***

The table below summarises the reactions of some metals with oxygen, water and dilute sulphuric acid.

<table>
<tr><th>Metal</th><th>Reaction with oxygen</th><th>Reaction with water</th><th>Reaction with dilute sulphuric acid</th></tr>
<tr><td>K</td><td rowspan="6">Burn when heated in oxygen to form the oxide</td><td rowspan="3">React with cold water to form hydrogen</td><td rowspan="2">Dangerously violent reaction</td></tr>
<tr><td>Na</td></tr>
<tr><td>Ca</td><td rowspan="4">React to give hydrogen</td></tr>
<tr><td>Mg</td><td>Slow reaction with cold water.<br>Reacts with steam</td></tr>
<tr><td>Zn</td><td rowspan="2">React with steam to give hydrogen</td></tr>
<tr><td>Fe</td></tr>
<tr><td>Cu</td><td>Oxide forms slowly.<br>Does not burn</td><td rowspan="3">No reaction with steam</td><td rowspan="3">No reaction</td></tr>
<tr><td>Silver</td><td rowspan="2">No reaction</td></tr>
<tr><td>Gold</td></tr>
</table>

Use the table to answer the following questions.

(a) In the series of experiments shown below (Figure 7.2) a piece of metal was placed in the solution shown.

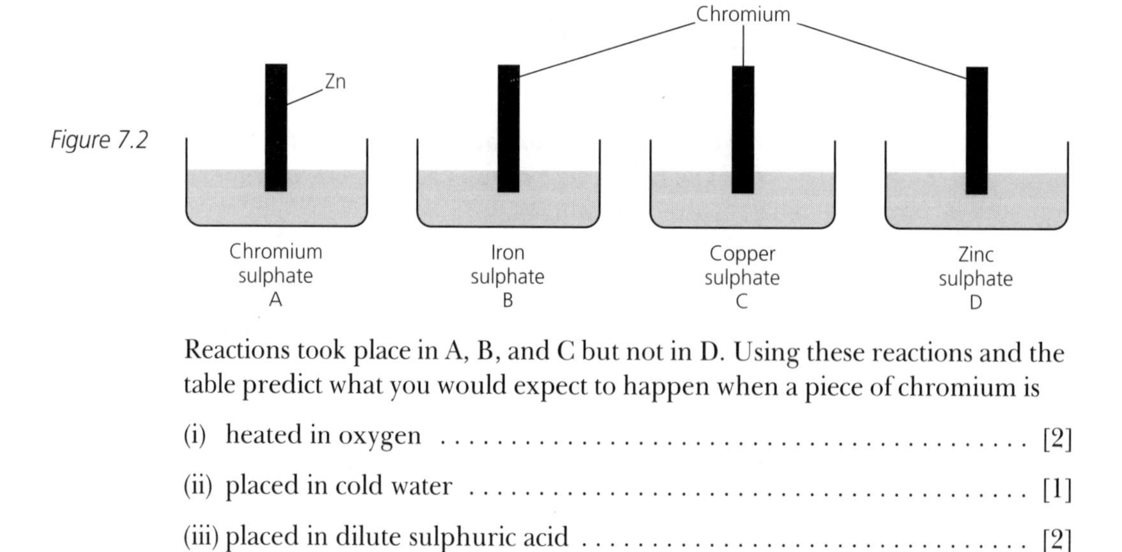


*Figure 7.2*

Reactions took place in A, B, and C but not in D. Using these reactions and the table predict what you would expect to happen when a piece of chromium is

(i) heated in oxygen .......................................... [2]

(ii) placed in cold water ...................................... [1]

(iii) placed in dilute sulphuric acid ............................ [2]

(b) Why is gold used in some dental treatments?

.................................................. [2]

(c) Give a word equation for the reaction of calcium with water

.................................................. [1]

(d) Give a symbol equation for the reaction of zinc with steam.

.................................................................... [2]

(e) Describe what would be observed when a piece of magnesium ribbon is placed in copper sulphate solution.

....................................................................

.................................................................... [2]

(f) Which **one** of the three metals iron, copper or magnesium would you use for making hot-water storage cylinders? Explain your answer.

....................................................................

.................................................................... [3]

**Total: 15 marks**
(NICCEA)

NOTE
*This question has a student answer with examiner's comments.* *See pp. 100–1.*

***Question 3 – Higher***

A class studied five different metals, labelled A, B, C, D and E. Some of the experiments were carried out by the teacher and some by the pupils. The results of the experiment are shown in the table.

| ***Metal*** | ***Result of heating in air*** | ***Reaction with cold water*** | ***Reaction with steam*** | ***Reaction with dilute acid*** |
|---|---|---|---|---|
| **A** | Did not burn. Oxide formed on surface. | No reaction. | Slow reaction. | Slow reaction. |
| **B** | No reaction. | No reaction. | No reaction. | No reaction. |
| **C** | It burns violently. Oxide formed. | Bubbles of hydrogen were quickly produced. | NOT ATTEMPTED. | NOT ATTEMPTED. |
| **D** | Did not burn. Oxide formed on surface. | No reaction. | No reaction. | No reaction. |
| **E** | It burned quickly. Oxide formed. | A few bubbles on the surface of the metal. | Vigorous reaction. Hydrogen and oxide produced. | Dissolved quickly. Hydrogen produced. |

(a) Use the results of the experiments to place the five metals , A, B, C, D and E, in order of reactivity.

Most reactive ........................................ Least reactive [4]

(b) Why were the reactions of metal C with steam or with acid **not** carried out?

.................................................................... [1]

(c) At the end of the lesson the teacher told the class that the five metals were calcium, copper, gold, iron and magnesium.
Use information from the Data Chapter on p. 117 to identify each of the metals A, B, C, D and E. ..................................................

.................................................................... [1]

(d) Explain in terms of their structure, **why** metals are good conductors of heat and electricity. ..................................................

.................................................................... [3]

**Total: 9 marks**
(NEAB)

# 8 Quantitative Chemistry

## REVISION TIPS

- Do not be afraid of numbers: the more you practice the better you will become.
- Make sure you understand the worked examples in this chapter.
- Do not take short cuts, you must show *all* your working.
- Spend time making sure that you have read the information correctly, e.g. if you read in a hurry you might confuse Mn (manganese) with Mg (magnesium).
- Make sure you understand what the formula means, e.g. $CuSO_4$ means that copper sulphate contains 1 copper atom, 1 sulphur atom and 4 oxygen atoms per formula of copper sulphate.
- Do not place too much faith in your calculator – make sure that your answer is sensible, e.g. if you are asked to find the charge on an ion, it must be a whole number and be either 1, 2 or 3; the charge will be positive if it is a metal and negative if it is a non-metal.
- Most calculations will be answers that can be worked out with or without a calculator. If you use a calculator, then do not write answers to several decimal places when answers to two decimal places will suffice.
- Always make sure that you have included units – a number such as 10 means nothing. Put in the units such as 10 grams or 10 litres or 10 moles.
- 1 litre $\equiv$ 1 $dm^3$.
- Make sure that you have learnt and understood *all* the definitions in this section, particularly the definition of the **mole**.
- Before you start answering a numerical question, you must ask yourself, **What is the problem?** You must focus all your attention on this objective.

## TOPIC OUTLINE

### Key definitions

- The **relative atomic mass** ($A_r$) of an atom is the mass of an atom on a scale where an atom of carbon-12 is 12.00.
- The **relative formula mass** is the sum of the relative atomic masses of the atoms in the formula. (The chemical can be either a covalent element, covalent compound or an ionic compound.)
- A **mole** is the amount of substance that contains the same number of particles as there are atoms in 12.00 grams of carbon-12. A mole contains $6 \times 10^{23}$ particles – it is called the **Avogadro's constant**.
- **Avogadro's Law** states that, 'Equal volumes of all gases under the same conditions of temperature and pressure contain the same number of molecules.'
- One **mole** of any gas under the same conditions of temperature and pressure occupies the same volume (24 litres at room temperature and pressure).
- A solution containing ONE mole of the solute in ONE litre of solution is called a **one molar** solution.

- A **Faraday** is a mole of electrons.
- A **coulomb** is the amount of electricity equivalent to one ampere flowing for one second.

## Relative formula mass (RFM)

When you are asked to work out the relative formula mass of a compound make sure you understand the formula of the compound. Relative atomic masses will either be given in the question or in a book of data.

### *Worked examples*

*Question 1 – Foundation*
*Calculate the relative formula mass (RFM) of the following compounds:*
*(Relative atomic masses: H = 1; C = 12; O = 16; Mg = 24 ; S = 32; Cu = 64)*

(a) *Magnesium oxide (MgO)*
Magnesium oxide contains ONE atom of magnesium and ONE atom of oxygen per formula.

Its RFM is $24 + 16 = \mathbf{40}$.

(b) *Water ($H_2O$)*
Each water molecule contains TWO atoms of hydrogen and ONE atom of oxygen.

Its RFM is $2 \times 1 + 16 = \mathbf{18}$.

(c) *Copper sulphate crystals ($CuSO_4.5H_2O$)*
This is a far more complicated example. The formula of copper sulphate crystals contain ONE atom of copper, ONE atom of sulphur, FOUR atoms of oxygen and FIVE molecules of water.

Its RFM is $64 + 32 + (4 \times 16) + (5 \times 18) = 64 + 32 + 64 + 90 = \mathbf{250}$.

Look at this example carefully. If you do not understand where the number 18 came from, look at example (b) above.

- Sometimes you are given the relative formula mass and you are asked to work out a relative atomic mass, and then use your data book to identify the element.

*Question 2*
*A compound $XCl_4$ has a relative formula mass of 349.*
(a) *What is the relative atomic mass of X? (Relative atomic mass of Cl = 35.5)*
$XCl_4$ contains ONE atom of X and FOUR atoms of chlorine.
The contribution of four atoms of chlorine is $4 \times 35.5 = 142$.
Therefore the relative atomic mass of X is $349 - 142 = 207$.
(b) *Which element does X represent? (You should use your data booklet to help you answer this question.)*
The element with a relative atomic mass of 207 is lead.

## Formula

> KEY POINT
> *The number of moles of an element can be found by dividing the mass of the element by its relative atomic mass.*

The number of moles of a compound can be found by dividing the mass of the compound by its relative formula mass.

***Worked example***

*It was found that 24 grams of a hydrocarbon contained 18 grams of carbon. What is the formula of the hydrocarbon? (Relative atomic masses: H = 1; C = 12)*

Remember that hydrocarbons contain carbon and hydrogen only and therefore the hydrocarbon must contain $24 - 18 = 6$ grams of hydrogen. 18 grams of carbon combines with 6 grams of hydrogen.

| | ***Carbon*** | ***Hydrogen*** |
|---|---|---|
| Mass | 18 g | 6 g |
| Moles $\left(\frac{mass}{A_r}\right)$ | $\frac{18}{12}$ | $\frac{6}{1}$ |
| Moles | 1.5 | 6 |
| Divide by smallest | 1 | 4 |

1 mole of carbon atoms combines with 4 moles of hydrogen atoms, therefore the formula is **$CH_4$**.

## Titrations

Titrations can be used to work out the **concentrations** of solutions. The number of moles of solute in 1 litre of solution can be calculated by dividing the number in grams per litre by the relative formula mass of the solute.

***Worked example***

*A student prepared 500 cm³ of a solution by dissolving 2.80 g of potassium hydroxide (KOH) in pure water. 25.0 cm³ of this solution exactly neutralised 20.0 cm³ of a solution of sulphuric acid. The equation for the reaction is:*

$$2KOH(aq) + H_2SO_4(aq) \rightarrow K_2SO_4(aq) + 2H_2O(l)$$

(a) *Calculate the concentration of the potassium hydroxide solution in moles per litre (mol/dm³). (Relative atomic masses H = 1; O = 16; K = 39)*

500 cm³ of solution contains 2.8 g of potassium hydroxide, therefore 1000 cm³ (1 litre) will contain $2 \times 2.8 = 5.6$ g of potassium hydroxide.

**RFM** of KOH $= 39 + 16 + 1 = 56$.

**Concentration of the solution** $\frac{5.6}{56} = 0.1$ moles per litre.

(b) *Use the result from (a) to calculate the concentration of sulphuric acid in moles per litre.*

Number of moles of KOH used

$$= 0.1 \times \frac{25}{1000} = 0.0025 \left[\frac{\text{molarity} \times \text{volume}}{1000} = \text{moles}\right]$$

from the equation TWO moles of KOH react with ONE mole of sulphuric acid, therefore the number of moles of sulphuric acid in 20 cm³ will be half the number of moles of potassium hydroxide $= \frac{0.0025}{2} = 0.00125$.

HINT
*Make sure you understand this calculation.*

Number of moles in 1000 cm³ $= 0.00125 \times \frac{1000}{20} =$ **0.0625 moles per litre**.

## Molar volume

**_Worked example_**

*The equation for the action of heat on sodium hydrogencarbonate is:*

$2NaHCO_3(s) \rightarrow Na_2CO_3(s) + H_2O(l) + CO_2(g)$

*Calculate the volume of carbon dioxide given off at room temperature and pressure when 21 g of sodium hydrogencarbonate is heated. (1 mole of gas occupies 24.0 litres ($dm^3$) at room temperature and pressure.)*

RFM of sodium hydrogencarbonate

$= 23 + 1 + 12 + (3 \times 16) = 23 + 1 + 12 + 48 = 84$

Number of moles of sodium hydrogencarbonate $= \frac{21}{84} = 0.25$

From the equation **2** moles of sodium hydrogencarbonate gives **1** mole of carbon dioxide therefore the number of moles of carbon dioxide formed

$= \frac{0.25}{2} = 0.125.$

Volume of carbon dioxide formed $= 0.125 \times 24 =$ **3.0 litres**.

## Faradays and coulombs

**_Worked example_**

*An electric current of 0.6 amp (A) was passed through dilute sulphuric acid for 16 minutes and during that time 72 $cm^3$ of hydrogen was collected at the negative electrode (cathode). (1 mole of hydrogen gas occupies 24 $dm^3$ under the conditions of the experiment and 1 Faraday is 96 000 coulombs of electricity per mole of electrons.)*

HINT
*Don't forget to convert minutes into seconds.*

Number of coulombs passed $= 0.6 \times 16 \times 60 = 576$ coulombs

Number of Faradays $= \frac{576}{96\,000} = 0.006$ Faradays

Number of moles of hydrogen in 72 $cm^3$ $= \frac{72}{24\,000} = 0.003$ moles

Thus 0.006 Faradays is required to discharge 0.003 mole of hydrogen gas.
Hence **2** Faradays is required to discharge **1** mole of hydrogen gas.
Since hydrogen is diatomic ($H_2$), and is discharged at the cathode, the charge on the ion is **+1**

$2H^+(aq) + 2e^- \rightarrow H_2(g)$

## REVISION ACTIVITIES

**1** Fill in the missing words:

(a) The relative . . . . . . . . . . . . . . . . mass of an element is the mass of an atom on a scale where an atom of carbon-12 has a mass of 12.00.

(b) The relative . . . . . . . . . . . . . . . . mass is the sum of the relative atomic masses of the atoms in the formula.

(c) A . . . . . . . . . . . . . . . . is the amount of a substance that contains the same number of particles as there are atoms in 12.00 grams of carbon-12.

(d) A . . . . . . . . . . . . . . . . is a mole of electrons.

2 Calculate the relative formula mass of the following:

(H = 1; C = 12; N = 14; O = 16; Mg = 24; S = 32)

(a) Ammonium nitrate ($NH_4NO_3$) ......................................

(b) Magnesium sulphate crystals ($MgSO_4.7H_2O$) ..........................

(c) Ethyl ethanoate ($CH_3CO_2C_2H_5$) ....................................

3 Calculate the number of moles for each of the following. (Relative atomic masses H = 1; C = 12; O = 16; Na = 23. One mole of a gas at room temperature and pressure occupies 24 litres.)

(a) 2 g of hydrogen molecules ......................................

(b) 318 g of sodium carbonate ($Na_2CO_3$) ..............................

(c) 48 litres of carbon dioxide at room temperature and pressure ..........

4 If 55 g of manganese combines with 32 g of oxygen, what is the formula of this oxide of manganese? (Relative atomic masses: O = 16; Mn = 55)

......................................................................

5 What is the molarity (measured in moles per litre) of 500 $cm^3$ of an aqueous solution containing 49 g of sulphuric acid ($H_2SO_4$)? (Relative atomic masses H = 1; O = 16: S = 32)

......................................................................

6 What volume of oxygen measured at room temperature and pressure will be given off when 50 $cm^3$ of 5.0 M hydrogen peroxide completely decomposes into oxygen and water. (1 mole of any gas occupies 24 $dm^3$ (litres) at room temperature and pressure.)

$2H_2O_2(aq) \rightarrow 2H_2O(l) + O_2(g)$

......................................................................

7 How many Faradays are required for each of the following electrode reactions?

(a) $Cu^{2+} \rightarrow Cu$ ......................................

(b) $2O^{2-} \rightarrow O_2$ ......................................

(c) $2Al^3 \rightarrow 2Al$ ......................................

## PRACTICE QUESTIONS

***Question 1 – Higher***

(a) 11.6 g of an oxide of iron was found to contain 8.4 g of iron. Calculate the formula of the oxide using the following procedure.

[$A_r$(O) = 16; $A_r$(Fe) = 56].

(i) Calculate the mass of oxygen in 11.6 g of the oxide.

...................................................................[1]

(ii) Using the masses and relative atomic masses of the elements, calculate the ratio of the number of atoms of iron to the number of atoms of oxygen.

......................................................................

...................................................................[2]

(iii) Calculate the formula of the oxide.

...................................................................[1]

(b) Iron reacts with a solution of copper(II) sulphate in accordance with the following equation.

$Fe(s) + CuSO_4(aq) \rightarrow FeSO_4(aq) + Cu(s)$

Copper used to be extracted from Parys Mountain in Anglesey. One method was to throw scrap iron into shallow lakes containing copper(II) sulphate. Calculate the mass of copper that would be obtained from 14 tonnes of iron.

.......................................................................

.......................................................................

....................................................................... [3]

**Total: 7 marks**
(WJEC part question)

***Question 2 – Higher***

Laboratory analysis shows that 15.15 g of chalcopyrite has the following composition by mass. Copper 5.27 g; iron 4.61 g. Sulphur is the only other element present.

(a) Use these figures to find the simplest formula of chalcopyrite.

.......................................................................

.......................................................................

....................................................................... [2]

(b) The iron content of the chalcopyrite is removed and copper(II) sulphide, CuS, is produced. This is heated in air to produce copper(II) oxide and sulphur dioxide.

(i) Write the balance equation for the reaction between copper(II) sulphide and air.

....................................................................... [2]

(ii) What is the maximum mass of copper(II) oxide which could be obtained from 960 kg of pure copper(II) sulphide?

.......................................................................

.......................................................................

.......................................................................

....................................................................... [2]

**Total: 8 marks**
(MEG)

***Question 3 – Higher***

Since 1850 most books and documents have been printed on acidic paper which, over time, becomes brittle and disintegrates. By treating books with diethyl zinc vapour the acids in the paper are neutralised. Diethyl zinc vapour penetrates the closed book and reacts with the small amount of water in the paper to form zinc oxide. The zinc oxide neutralises acids and protects the book from acids that may be formed later. There is no visible difference between untreated and treated books.

The reaction between diethyl zinc and water is represented by the equation:

$Zn(C_2H_5)_2(g) + H_2O(l) \rightarrow ZnO(s) + 2C_2H_6(g)$

(a) The total moisture content of a book which was to be treated was found to be 0.9 g water.

(Relative atomic masses: H = 1, C = 12, O = 16, Zn = 65)

(one mole of diethyl zinc molecules at room temperature and pressure occupies 24 litres)

(i) How many moles of water were present in the book?

. . . . . . . . . . . . . . . . . . . . . . . . . . . . . . . . . . . . . . . . . . . . . . . . . . . . . . [2]

(ii) Using the equation, how many moles of diethyl zinc would react with this number of moles of water?

. . . . . . . . . . . . . . . . . . . . . . . . . . . . . . . . . . . . . . . . . . . . . . . . . . . . . . [1]

(iii) What is the volume at room temperature and pressure of this number of moles of diethyl zinc vapour?

. . . . . . . . . . . . . . . . . . . . . . . . . . . . . . . . . . . . . . . . . . . . . . . . . . . . . . [1]

(iv) What mass of zinc oxide would be formed in the book?

. . . . . . . . . . . . . . . . . . . . . . . . . . . . . . . . . . . . . . . . . . . . . . . . . . . . . . [2]

(b) The acid content of the book was found to be 0.032 mole of $H^+(aq)$.
The equation for the reaction between zinc oxide and acid is:

$ZnO(s) + 2H^+(aq) \rightarrow Zn^{2+}(aq) + H_2O(l)$

Calculate the mass of zinc oxide required to neutralise the acid in the book and hence the mass of the excess zinc oxide which remains in the book.

. . . . . . . . . . . . . . . . . . . . . . . . . . . . . . . . . . . . . . . . . . . . . . . . . . . . . . . . .

. . . . . . . . . . . . . . . . . . . . . . . . . . . . . . . . . . . . . . . . . . . . . . . . . . . . . . . . .

. . . . . . . . . . . . . . . . . . . . . . . . . . . . . . . . . . . . . . . . . . . . . . . . . . . . . . [3]

**Total: 14 marks**
(NEAB)

NOTE
*This question has a student answer with examiner's comments.* *See p. 102.*

***Question 4 – Foundation***

(a) Calculate the relative formula masses for the following compounds.
(Relative atomic masses:

H = 1, C = 12, O = 16, Na = 23, S = 32, Cl = 35.5, Ca = 40, Cu = 64.)

(i) NaCl . . . . . . . . . . . . . . . . . . . . . . . . . . . . . . . . . . . . . . . . . . . . . . . . . [1]

(ii) $CaCl_2$ . . . . . . . . . . . . . . . . . . . . . . . . . . . . . . . . . . . . . . . . . . . . . . . . . [1]

(iii) $C_6H_6$ . . . . . . . . . . . . . . . . . . . . . . . . . . . . . . . . . . . . . . . . . . . . . . . . . [1]

(iv) $CuSO_4.5H_2O$ . . . . . . . . . . . . . . . . . . . . . . . . . . . . . . . . . . . . . . . . . . . . [3]

(b) A compound $MBr_4$ has a relative formula mass of 439.

(i) What is the relative atomic mass of M? (Relative atomic mass: Br = 80)

. . . . . . . . . . . . . . . . . . . . . . . . . . . . . . . . . . . . . . . . . . . . . . . . . . . . . . . .

. . . . . . . . . . . . . . . . . . . . . . . . . . . . . . . . . . . . . . . . . . . . . . . . . . . . . . . .

. . . . . . . . . . . . . . . . . . . . . . . . . . . . . . . . . . . . . . . . . . . . . . . . . . . . . . [3]

(ii) Which element does M represent? (You should use the Data Pages to help you answer this question) . . . . . . . . . . . . . . . . . . . . . . . . . . . . . . . . . [1]

**Total: 10 marks**
(NICCEA)

# 9 The Earth and its atmosphere

## REVISION TIPS

- Draw up a **comparative list** of the gases present in the atmosphere originally (4 billion years ago) and at present.
- Draw and learn the significance of the three major cycles responsible for the present balance of gases in the atmosphere:
  - the Carbon cycle
  - the Nitrogen cycle
  - the Water cycle
- Draw a fully labelled cross-section of the Earth showing its layered structure.
- Draw up a full-page table of the three main rock types: igneous; sedimentary and metamorphic: State:
  - How, and from what, they are formed.
  - Their main structural features [crystal size, layers etc.].
  - Named examples with everyday uses.
  - Relative ages.
- Draw large diagrams of the following for quick reference:
  - the rock cycle
  - an identification key for rock types
- Draw labelled **cross-sections** of:
  - Oceanic plates sliding past each other – San Andreas Fault.
  - Sea floor spreading/oceanic plates diverging – Mid-Atlantic Ridge formation.
  - Oceanic and continental plates colliding – Andean Mountain range formation.
  - A volcano – showing **intrusive** and **extrusive** igneous rock formations.
- Study maps showing:
  - The positions of major **continents** 200 million years ago and today.
  - The positions of **plate boundaries** noting the occurrence of volcanoes and earthquakes.

HINT
*It is not necessary to memorise the detail of these maps.*

## TOPIC OUTLINE

*Note* that this topic is not included in the NICCEA syllabus.

### Key definitions

- The **ozone layer** is a layer in the stratosphere which filters out harmful ultra violet (u.v.) radiation from the sun.
- **Igneous** rock forms by the crystallisation, on cooling, of molten magma.
- **Sedimentary** rock is made up of rock particles deposited in layers and converted into rock by the weight of overlying material.
- **Metamorphic** rock forms from sedimentary and igneous rock subjected to intense pressure and/or heat. It looks like bands of interlocking crystals.

HINT
*You can remember the three types of rock by **ISM** (igneous, sedimentary, metamorphic).*

- **Weathering** is the disintegration of rock by either the action of water freezing in cracks or acidic rain or plant roots.
- **Erosion** is the removal of weathered material by the action of wind, water, ice and gravity.
- **Transportation** is the carriage of rock debris by water, wind and ice to the final place of sedimentation – usually in a lake or the ocean.
- **Lithification** (literally rock formation) is the result of pressure from the weight of overlying sediment.
- **Continental drift** is the separation process which produced the present continents.
- **Tectonic plates** are the six major, and many smaller, rigid plates making up the top 100 km or so of the Earth's surface.

## Evolution of the Earth's atmosphere

The Earth's atmosphere has evolved over 4000 million years. **Gases** in the atmosphere could have come from:

- **volcanic activity** – ammonia , methane, oxides of carbon , hydrogen sulphide, noble gases.
- The **action of sunlight** on water vapour producing hydrogen and oxygen; and on ammonia producing nitrogen and hydrogen.
- Reaction between some of the above gases under favourable conditions – sulphur dioxide, carbon dioxide.

HINT
*Hydrogen, the lightest known gas, has long since escaped into space by **diffusion**.*

Evolution of life would have changed the atmosphere even more drastically.

- Life required a special set of conditions to start. This would include the appropriate chemicals and climatic conditions.
- The first life was probably **bacteria** and **blue-green algae** which could live on carbon compounds and ammonia. Some of these bacteria would have been able to produce **nitrogen** from ammonia and nitrates (study the Nitrogen cycle).
- Later, **plants** evolved which produced **oxygen** by photosynthesis as they used up the abundant **carbon dioxide**.
- **Oxygen** acted upon by sunlight formed the **ozone layer**.
- **Plankton** in the oceans also consumed **carbon dioxide**, locking it up in their shells as calcium carbonate which eventually became seabed deposits and finally sedimentary deposits of limestone and chalk.
- As plants and plankton multiplied the **oxygen** content of the atmosphere increased and the **carbon dioxide** content further decreased.

For the past 200 million years the composition of the atmosphere has been roughly what it is today. This is largely because of the opposing processes:

- Volcanic activity, combustion of fossil fuels and animal respiration give out carbon dioxide.
- The reaction of carbon dioxide with sea water converts it into insoluble carbonates and soluble hydrogencarbonates (study the Carbon cycle).

KEY POINT
*The atmosphere today is 78% nitrogen; 21% oxygen 0.9% argon 0.038% carbon dioxide and a variable proportion of water vapour.*

## The Earth

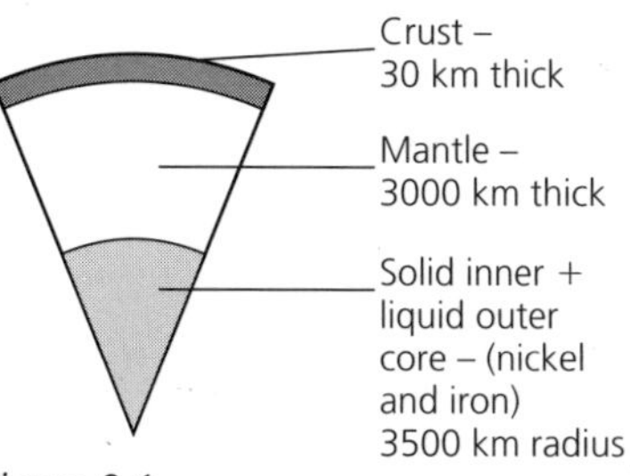


*Figure 9.1*
Cross section of the Earth

- **Structure**: See Fig. 9.1.
- **Magnetism**: the Earth is a giant magnet with magnetic poles close to the present geographical N- and S- poles. Poles have wandered in the past.
- **Oceans**: cover 70% of the Earth's surface.

## Rocks

There are three main types of rock: igneous, sedimentary and metamorphic. Make sure you can distinguish between the types and their formation.

### *Igneous rock*

Igneous rock is of two types: granite and basalt.

- **Granite** forms when magma solidifies slowly at depth in formations called **intrusions** – crystal grains are large.
- **Basalt** forms when magma is **extruded** from volcanoes and **solidifies rapidly** – crystal grains are small.

### *Sedimentary rock*

Sedimentary rock forms from other rocks by the following sequence of processes.

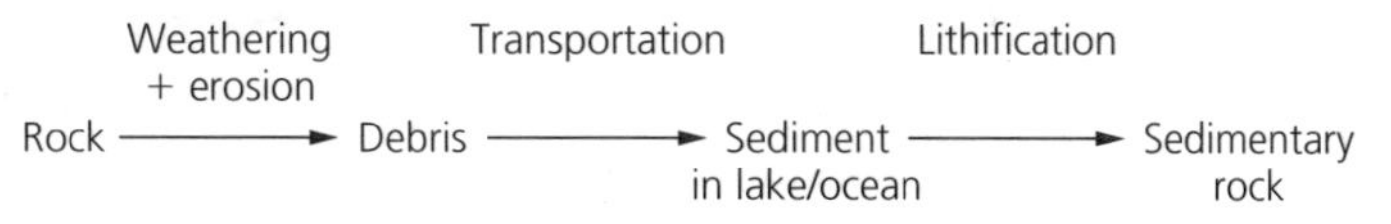


*Figure 9.2* Sequence of events in the formation of sedimentary rock

> KEY POINT
> *Lithification results from the combined processes of **compaction, cementation** and **hardening**.*

Examples of sedimentary rocks are:

- **Sandstone** – sand grains cemented together with calcite ($CaCO_3$).
- **Limestone** – from the dead bodies of countless shelled sea creatures.
- **Shale** – lithified mud.
- **Coal** – product of slow, anaerobic, decay of plant remains formed long ago.
- **Rock salt** – evaporated sea water plus other sediments.

### *Metamorphic rock.*

Metamorphic rocks are found in mountain ranges because of the high temperatures and pressures created by mountain-building processes.

Examples of metamorphic rock are:

- **Slate** is metamorphosed shale.
- **Marble** is metamorphosed limestone.
- **Sch**ist is metamorphosed **sh**ale.
- **G**neiss is metamorphosed **g**ranite.

> HINT
> *Note the letters in **bold** are to help you remember the origin of schist and gneiss.*

### *The Rock Cycle*

- Any type of rock can become the **source material** for sedimentary deposits.
- Sedimentary rock can be subjected to high temperature and/or pressure to become metamorphic rock.
- Metamorphic and sedimentary rock, if melted, become part of the reservoir of magma that may form igneous rock.
- The oldest rocks are igneous in origin.
- Metamorphic rock must be younger than the sedimentary/igneous rock it was formed from.
- An intrusive igneous rock must be younger than the surrounding rock.

> HINT
> *Fossils can be used to identify rocks of the same age in different places and to place rocks in a time sequence.*

***Rock identification – some pointers***

- Igneous rocks – basalt is dark and granite is light in colour.
- Igneous and metamorphic rocks are harder than sedimentary rock.
- Limestone (sedimentary) and marble (metamorphic) fizz with dilute hydrochloric acid because they give off carbon dioxide.
- Fossils can only exist in sedimentary rocks.
- Layers of grains or fragments show sedimentary origin.
- Metamorphosed rock may be **banded** – show light and dark layers, e.g. gneiss.

***Uses of rocks***

- **Granite**, **limestone** and **sandstone** - building materials and road foundation - called 'metalling'.
- **Slate** – roofing tiles.
- **Marble** and **slate** – monuments.
- **Limestone** and **clay/shale** mixtures – when roasted, form cement.
- **Limestone** – heated to 1000 °C in lime kilns, forms quicklime. This is slaked with water to form lime used in agriculture.

## Continental Drift and Plate Tectonics

- Two hundred million years ago the present continents were joined together in a single land mass called **Pangaea**, which eventually broke up.
- Continents have drifted apart because each forms part of a separate mass called a **tectonic plate**.
- Evidence for continental drift includes:
  - The shapes of West African and South American coastlines fit quite closely together.
  - These two continents have similar rocks and fossils.
  - The magnetic record of the **southern continents** show they were close together 150–200 million years ago.

***Plate tectonic theory***

Plate tectonic theory states that:

1. There are six large plates and some smaller ones covering the Earth.
2. The plates float on the mantle and their movement is driven by convection currents in the mantle. The plates move only a few centimetres a year.
3. Plates interact where they come into contact – at **plate margins**.

The **three** main types of interaction and their consequences are:

- Plates **slide past** each other – e.g. San Andreas Fault (earthquakes) see Figure 9.3.

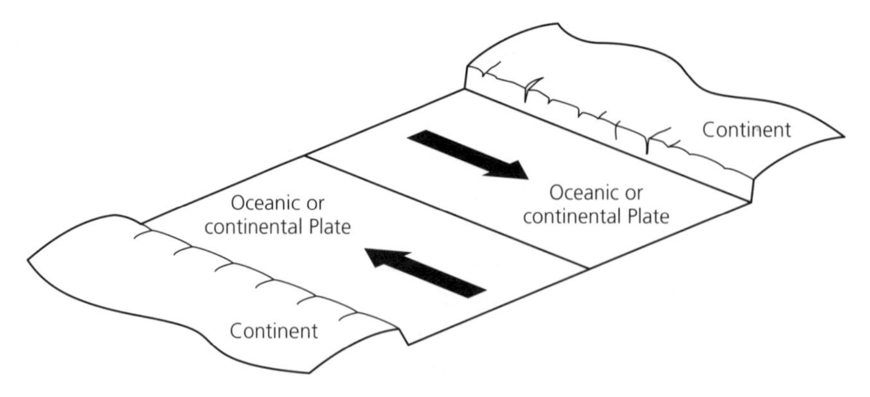


*Figure 9.3* Plates sliding past each other – San Andreas Fault

- Plates **move towards** each other. As they do, the denser oceanic plate is driven down (**subducted**) below the less dense continental plate. The oceanic plate melts and the continental crust is forced upwards forming mountains – e.g. Andean Mountain Range (earthquakes and volcanoes) and an ocean trench, see Figure 9.4.

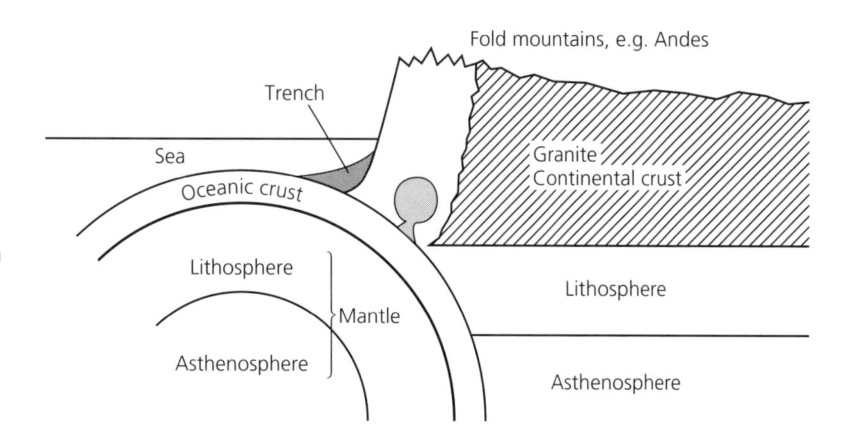


*Figure 9.4* Plates in collision – the Andean Mountain Range and ocean

- Plates **move away from** each other. Magma rises to fill the gap and produces new, basaltic, ocean crust. This is called sea-floor **spreading** – e.g. Mid-Atlantic Ridge (volcanoes), see Figure 9.5.

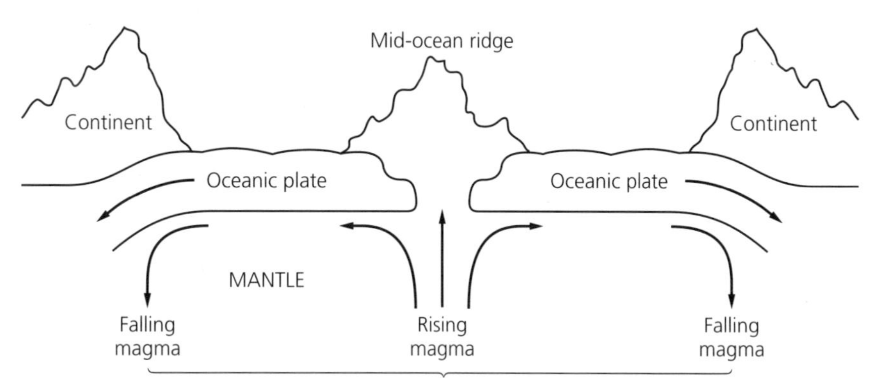


*Figure 9.5* Plates diverging – the Mid-Atlantc Ridge

## REVISION ACTIVITIES

1 Fill in the missing spaces.

(a) Two gases present in the atmosphere of the Earth before plant life evolved which are not common in today's atmosphere are

. . . . . . . . . . . . . . . . and . . . . . . . . . . . . . . . . .

(b) What change in the Earth's surface allowed the formation of the first seas?

. . . . . . . . . . . . . . . . . . . . . . . . . . . . . . . . . . . . . . . . . . . . . . . . . . . . . . . . . . .

(c) Fill in the three blank parts of the Rock cycle diagram at the top of the following page.

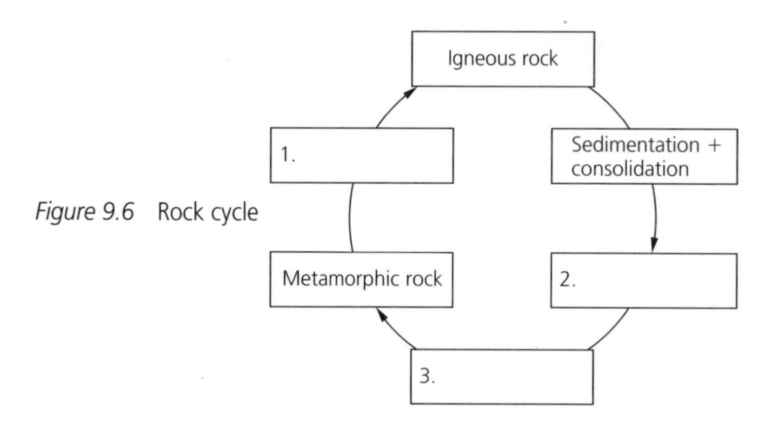

*Figure 9.6* Rock cycle

(d) Complete the table.

*Figure 9.7*

| ***Rock*** | ***Example*** | ***Conditions for formation*** | ***One use*** |
|---|---|---|---|
| Igneous | Granite | (i) . . . . . . . . . . . . . . . . . . | (ii) . . . . . . . . . . . |
| Sedimentary | (iii) . . . . . . . . . . . | (iv) . . . . . . . . . . . . . . . . . | Building stone |
| Metamorphic | (v) . . . . . . . . . . . | Heat and/or high pressure | (vi) . . . . . . . . . . . |

(e) Present-day continents are the result of crustal movements known as

. . . . . . . . . . . . . . . . . .

**2** Give a one-line explanation of the saltiness of the oceans.

. . . . . . . . . . . . . . . . . . . . . . . . . . . . . . . . . . . . . . . . . . . . . . . . . . . . . . . . . . . .

**3** The interaction of plates releases energy which causes . . . . . . . . . . . . . . . . . and . . . . . . . . . . . . . . . . activity.

**4** Complete the labelling of the diagram of a **long-extinct volcano** shown below in Figure 9.8.

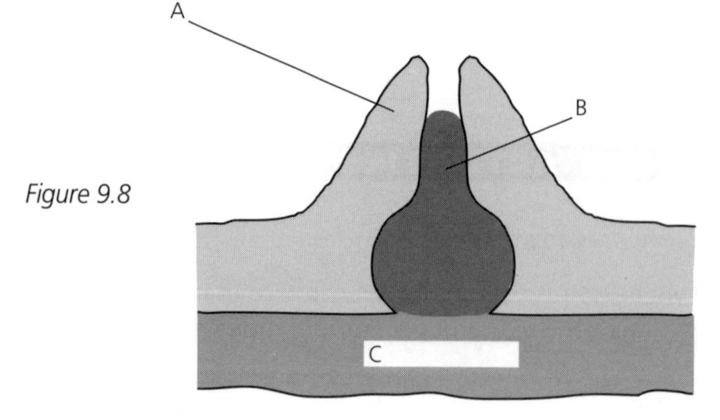

*Figure 9.8*

Rock-type A is . . . . . . . . . . . . . . . . . . . Rock-type B is . . . . . . . . . . . . . . . . . .

and C is . . . . . . . . . . . . . . . . . .

**5** Give one named **geographical place** or **region** where each of the following is occurring:

(a) Tectonic plates are sliding past each other. ........................

(b) Oceanic plates are moving apart. ................................

(c) An oceanic plate is colliding with a continental plate. ................

## PRACTICE QUESTIONS

***Question 1 – Higher***

(a) The diagram shows part of the water cycle.

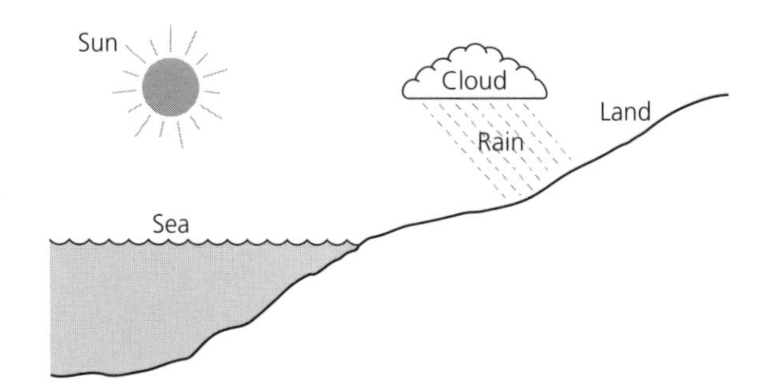


*Figure 9.9* Water cycle

Explain the water cycle. In your answer write about:

- how the Sun starts the water cycle;
- how the clouds and rain are formed;
- how the rain water goes back to the sea.

..........................................................................

..........................................................................

..........................................................................

..........................................................................

..........................................................................

..........................................................................

..........................................................................

..........................................................................

..........................................................................

..........................................................................

.......................................................................... [5]

(b) (i) Rainwater can cause the weathering of rocks. What type of rock is formed from the deposition, burial and compression of weathered rock fragments?

.......................................................................... [1]

(ii) Below is a flow diagram of the rock cycle. Correctly label each of the empty boxes using the words: **igneous rocks** **metamorphic rocks** **sedimentary rocks**

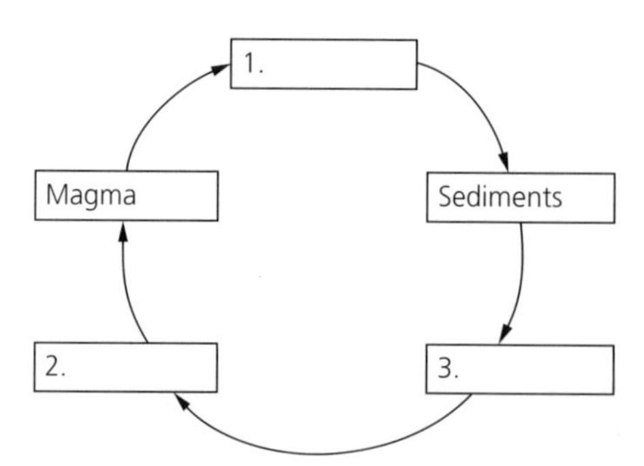


*Figure 9.10* Rock cycle

[2]

(iii) Limestone and marble are both forms of calcium carbonate. Limestone often contains fossils. Marble does not contain fossils. Explain why.

. . . . . . . . . . . . . . . . . . . . . . . . . . . . . . . . . . . . . . . . . . . . . . . . . . . . . . . . . . . .

. . . . . . . . . . . . . . . . . . . . . . . . . . . . . . . . . . . . . . . . . . . . . . . . . . . . . . . . . . . .

. . . . . . . . . . . . . . . . . . . . . . . . . . . . . . . . . . . . . . . . . . . . . . . . . . . . . . . . . . . .

. . . . . . . . . . . . . . . . . . . . . . . . . . . . . . . . . . . . . . . . . . . . . . . . . . . . . . . . . . . .

. . . . . . . . . . . . . . . . . . . . . . . . . . . . . . . . . . . . . . . . . . . . . . . . . . . . . . . . . . [2]

**Total: 10 marks**
(SEG)

***Question 2 – Higher***

The diagram shows a cross-section of a type of volcano.

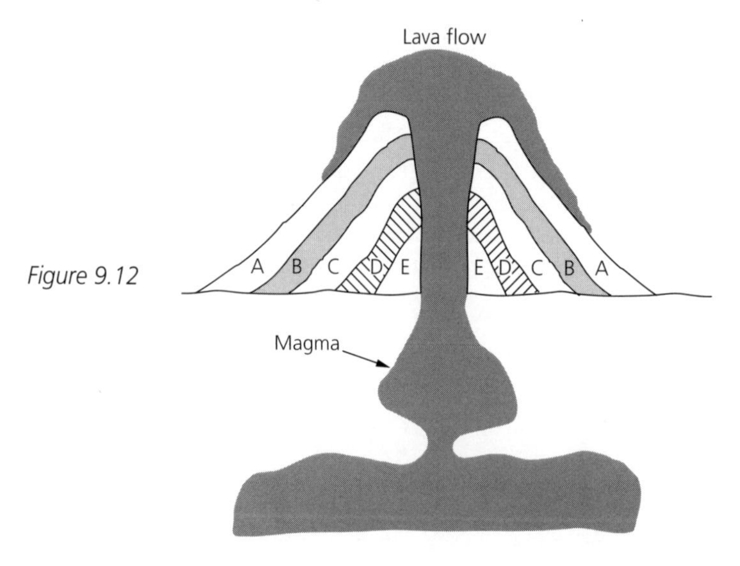


*Figure 9.12*

(a) What type of rocks are produced by volcanoes?

. . . . . . . . . . . . . . . . . . . . . . . . . . . . . . . . . . . . . . . . . . . . . . . . . . . . . . . . . . [1]

(b) Which of the labelled layers, A,B,C,D or E, is the oldest?

. . . . . . . . . . . . . . . . . . . . . . . . . . . . . . . . . . . . . . . . . . . . . . . . . . . . . . . . . . [1]

(c) Explain why the crystals on the surface of rock layer A are smaller than the crystals in the middle of the same layer.

. . . . . . . . . . . . . . . . . . . . . . . . . . . . . . . . . . . . . . . . . . . . . . . . . . . . . . . . . . . . . .

. . . . . . . . . . . . . . . . . . . . . . . . . . . . . . . . . . . . . . . . . . . . . . . . . . . . . . . . . . . . . .

. . . . . . . . . . . . . . . . . . . . . . . . . . . . . . . . . . . . . . . . . . . . . . . . . . . . . . . . . . . . [2]

**Total: 4 marks**

(MEG)

***Question 3 – Higher***

(a)Convection currents occur in the molten mantle of the Earth. The diagram represents the structure of the inside of the Earth.

*Figure 9.13*

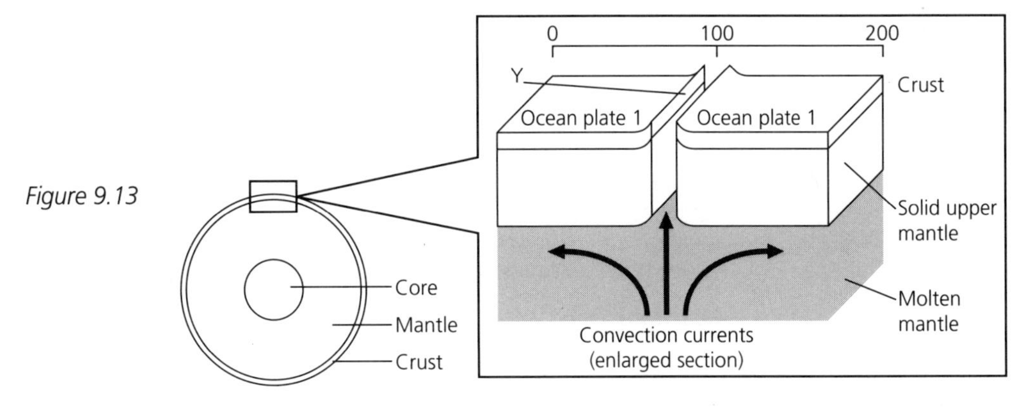


(i) Describe what you might expect to find at Y.

. . . . . . . . . . . . . . . . . . . . . . . . . . . . . . . . . . . . . . . . . . . . . . . . . . . . . . . . . . . . . .

. . . . . . . . . . . . . . . . . . . . . . . . . . . . . . . . . . . . . . . . . . . . . . . . . . . . . . . . . . . . [1]

(ii) Suggest **two** effects that the convection currents would have on the ocean plates. . . . . . . . . . . . . . . . . . . . . . . . . . . . . . . . . . . . . . . . . . . . . . . . .

. . . . . . . . . . . . . . . . . . . . . . . . . . . . . . . . . . . . . . . . . . . . . . . . . . . . . . . . . . . . . .

. . . . . . . . . . . . . . . . . . . . . . . . . . . . . . . . . . . . . . . . . . . . . . . . . . . . . . . . . . . . . .

. . . . . . . . . . . . . . . . . . . . . . . . . . . . . . . . . . . . . . . . . . . . . . . . . . . . . . . . . . . . [2]

(b) The diagram shows how the map of the Earth has changed over the past 200 million years.

*Figure 9.14*

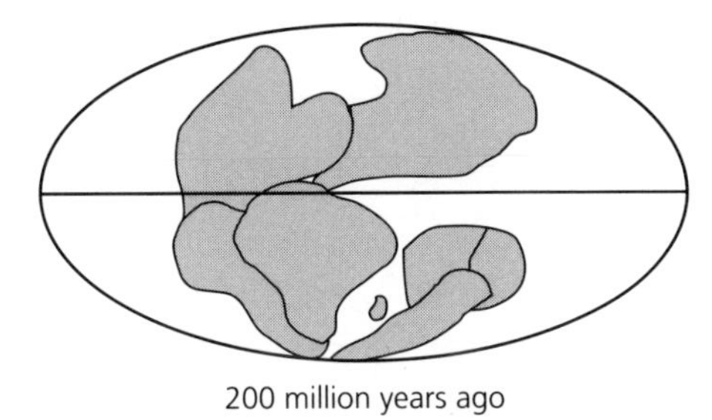


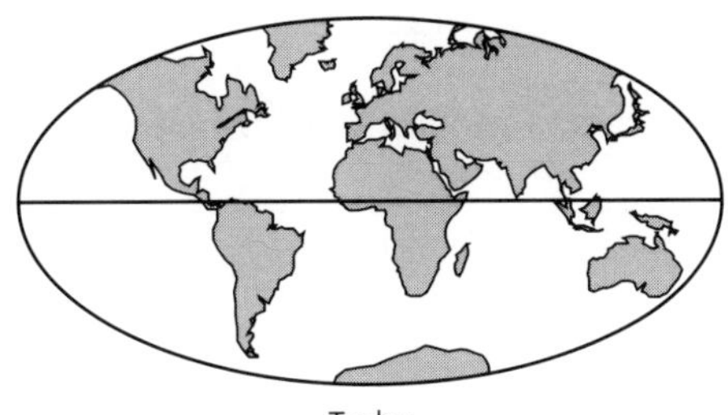

Suggest how this change could have happened, and what might happen to the continents during the next 200 million years.

. . . . . . . . . . . . . . . . . . . . . . . . . . . . . . . . . . . . . . . . . . . . . . . . . . . .

. . . . . . . . . . . . . . . . . . . . . . . . . . . . . . . . . . . . . . . . . . . . . . . . . . . .

. . . . . . . . . . . . . . . . . . . . . . . . . . . . . . . . . . . . . . . . . . . . . . . . . . . .

. . . . . . . . . . . . . . . . . . . . . . . . . . . . . . . . . . . . . . . . . . . . . . . . . . [4]

**Total: 7 marks**
(MEG)

NOTE
*This question has a student answer with examiner's comments.* *See p. 103.*

***Question 4 – Higher***

Igneous rocks are formed when molten magma from deep inside the Earth cools and becomes solid. Granite and basalt are examples of igneous rocks.

(a) The table shows the minerals found in samples of granite and basalt.

*Figure 9.15*

| ***Rock*** | ***Minerals*** | | |
|---|---|---|---|
| Granite | Feldspare | Mica | Quartz |
| Basalt | Augite | Feldspar | Olivine |

State **two** reasons why samples of freshly broken granite from different places may look different. . . . . . . . . . . . . . . . . . . . . . . . . . . . . . . . . . . . . . . .

. . . . . . . . . . . . . . . . . . . . . . . . . . . . . . . . . . . . . . . . . . . . . . . . . . [2]

(b) There are two types of igneous rock. Some information about them is shown in the table below.

*Figure 9.16*

| ***Rock type*** | ***Information about rock*** |
|---|---|
| Intrusive, e.g. granite | Solidifies inside the Earth's crust. This type of rock appears on the surface when the covering rocks are worn away. |
| Extrusive, e.g. basalt | Forms when liquid magma solidifies on the surface of the Earth. |

Describe **two** ways in which the appearance of samples of granite and basalt will differ.

. . . . . . . . . . . . . . . . . . . . . . . . . . . . . . . . . . . . . . . . . . . . . . . . . . . .

. . . . . . . . . . . . . . . . . . . . . . . . . . . . . . . . . . . . . . . . . . . . . . . . . . [2]

(c) Sugarloaf Mountain is a mountain in Brazil. It is on the site where there was once a volcano. It is made of intrusive igneous rock, and has the shape shown below.

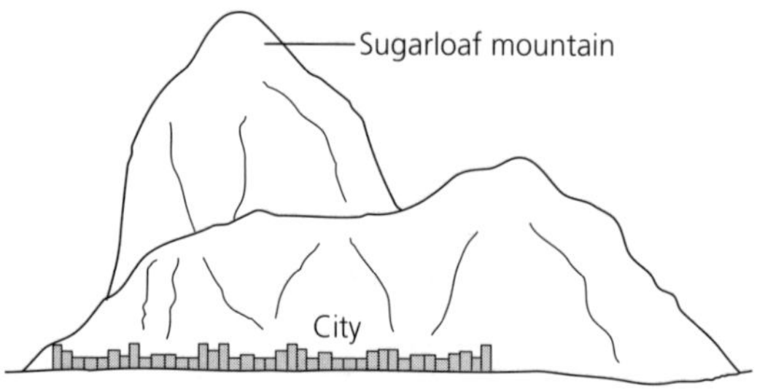

*Figure 9.17*

Suggest how this mountain was formed and why it is still there today.

. . . . . . . . . . . . . . . . . . . . . . . . . . . . . . . . . . . . . . . . . . . . . . . . . . . .

. . . . . . . . . . . . . . . . . . . . . . . . . . . . . . . . . . . . . . . . . . . . . . . . . . [2]

**Total: 6 marks**
(MEG)

*part III*

# Answers and grading

# 1 Solutions
# States of matter, elements mixtures and compounds

## SOLUTIONS TO REVISION ACTIVITIES

**1** solids, far apart
**2** melting point, move about (around)
**3** diffusion
**4** heat energy
**5** separate, two
**6** (a) filtration (b) chromatography (c) fractional distillation
(d) crystallisation
**7** copper – electrical wiring; making brass or bronze.
sulphuric acid – in lead-acid batteries or to make (superphosphate) fertiliser.
brine(salt solution) – to make chlorine or sodium hydroxide (by electrolysis).

## SOLUTIONS TO PRACTICE QUESTIONS

### *Question 1 – Foundation*

(a) Correct name [1] and corresponding symbol [1] of **any** element.
(b) Correct name [1] and corresponding formula [1] of **any** compound.
(c) (i) Name – such as sea water; tap water; mortar etc. [1]
(ii) Use – to obtain chlorine; drinking/washing; building with bricks etc. [1]
(iii) Name – could be water [1] in all the examples quoted in part (i).
(d) Box 1 – element; box 2 – mixture; box 3 – compound. If all three are labelled correctly [2], if only one is labelled correct [1].
(e) Gas [1] because there is plenty of space between the particles. [1]

**Total: 11 marks**

### *Question 2 – Foundation*

(a) **A** – gas or vapour [1]; **B** – liquid [1]; **C** – solid [1].

(b) (i) Second box – if liquid, the particles should be randomly arranged and very close with some touching. [1]
Third box – if gas, the particles should be well spaced out and few in number. [1]
(ii) Particles gain energy [1] they vibrate faster [1] and move further apart [1].

**Total: 8 marks**

### *Question 3 – Foundation*

(a) liquid [1] (b) gas [1] (c) solid [1] (d) gas [1].

**Total: 4 marks**

### *Question 4 – Higher*

**First process** – addition of water. Purpose – to dissolve the salt [1].
**Second process** – stirring. Purpose – to speed up dissolving [1].

**Third process** – filtration. Purpose – to remove insoluble material [1].
**Fourth process** – evaporation. Purpose – to remove most of the water/ to form a saturated solution [1].
**Fifth process** – crystallisation. Purpose – to form crystals of pure sodium chloride/ salt [1].

**Total: 5 marks**

***Question 5 – Student answer***

(a) (i) Because petrol fumes leak ✓ out from the open tank ✓ and then diffuse ✓ up to the motorist's nose.

***Examiner's note*** A good response. Petrol could also spill and then evaporate but your fume escape is more common.

(ii) Diffusion is faster ✓ if gases are hotter ✓

***Examiner's note*** A good answer – full marks.

(b) Oil doesn't evaporate as fast ✓ as petrol because it is thicker. ✗ Therefore the molecules can't escape as fast. ✓

***Examiner's note*** 2 points out of 3. Oil *is* thicker than petrol, but the **reason** for its slower evaporation is its larger molecules – which is also the reason for its higher viscosity.

(c) Tyres get hot ✓ on long journeys. Therefore the rubber ✗ and the air inside expands ✓. This causes the pressure increase. ✓

***Examiner's note*** 3 out of 4. You did not complete the explanation by mentioning the fact that the volume of air must remain constant for the pressure to increase with temperature rise.

10 out of 12. An excellent mark worth a grade A on this Higher level question.

# 2 Solutions
# *Atomic structure, bonding and the Periodic Table*

## SOLUTIONS TO REVISION ACTIVITIES

**1** 2,8,1; potassium
**2** (a) (i) carbon; hydrogen (ii) double
(b) (i) two (ii) four shared electrons make a double bond
**3** (a) Eight **additional** electrons must be inserted on the diagram. There should be four **shared** electrons; two **pairs** of electrons in the outer shell of the right-hand oxygen atom; and two electrons in the inner shell of the right-hand oxygen atom.
(b) The 'dot and cross diagram' should show the following electron structures:
- a magnesium atom 2,8,2
- an oxygen atom 2,6
- a magnesium ion 2,8 with a charge of $2^+$
- an oxide ion 2,8 with a charge of $2^-$

**4** atomic (proton) numbers; Periodic Table; Mendeleev
**5** periods
**6** electrons

**7** left; right
**8.** halogens; less
**9** alkaline; hydrogen
**10** (a) He (b) helium balloons or deep-sea divers 'air' supply
(c) sodium hydroxide (d) copper (e) Cu (f) $Cl_2$ (g) sterilising household water supplies (h) sodium hypochlorite (i) domestic bleach

## SOLUTIONS TO PRACTICE QUESTIONS

***Question 1 – Foundation***

(a) Any **two** of lithium, sodium, potassium, rubidium or caesium. [2].
(b) (i) Group VII or seven. [1]
(ii) The Halogens. [1]
(iii) Any **two** of fluorine, chlorine, bromine or iodine. [2]
(c) (i) The Noble gases. [1]
(ii) Any **one** of helium, neon, argon, krypton, xenon or radon. [1]
(d) (i) Rubidium will be more reactive than sodium. [1]
(ii) $Rb_2CO_3$ [1] the symbol Na is replaced by Rb.
(e) (i) $MCl_3$ [1]
(ii) $M_2O_3$ [1]

HINT
*Be careful! question (b) could be misread as a **non-reactive group** of non-metals – which is what the next question asks for.*

**Total: 12 marks**

***Question 2 – Higher***

(a) Draw diagrams of atoms for both aluminium and phosphorus. Each diagram of the atoms should have three concentric circles with electrons in order from the inner to outer circles as follows:
(i) 2,8, 3 [One mark for the inner two electrons 2,8, the second mark for the outer three electrons.]
(ii) 2,8,5 [One mark for the inner two electrons 2,8, the second mark for the outer five electrons.]
(b) Fluorine [1].
(c) (i) A brown/red/reddy-brown colour appears [1]
(ii) $Cl_2 + 2KBr \rightarrow 2KCl + Br_2$, **OR**
$Cl_2 + 2Br^- \rightarrow 2Cl^- + Br_2$
[One mark for left-hand side; One mark for right-hand side of the equation as written.]
(d)

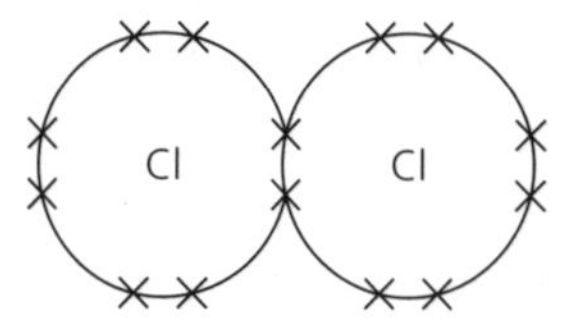

*Figure A2.1*

[One mark for **two atoms** in the molecule. One mark for the correct number of electrons (14) in the **outer shells**. One mark for showing **one shared pair** of electrons.]
(e) (i) $CaCl_2$ (ii) $GeCl_4$ [One mark for each correct formula.]
(f) (i) Silicon or germanium (on the metal/non-metal boundary). [1]
(ii) Carbon/graphite. [1]
Explanation: Graphite contains free electrons [1] which allow the current to pass or which move through the solid as an electrical current. [1]

**Total: 17 marks**

### *Question 3 – Higher*

(a) Element – a substance that contains atoms of the same atomic number; contains atoms of one type only; cannot be broken down into anything simpler. Any **one** of these. [1]
Compound – a substance containing more than one type of atom **bonded together**. [1]

(b) Magnesium atom to show the electron structure 2,8,2. [1]
Chlorine to show the electron structure 2,8,7. [1]

(c) Magnesium atom loses two [1] electrons [1], or forms 2,8 structure [1].
Chlorine atom gains one [1] electron [1], or forms 2,8,8 structure [1].
**Any** four points for the full marks.

(d) Ionic bonding – magnesium and chloride ions [1] are attracted by their opposite charges [1] forming the ionic bond.

**Total: 10 marks**

### *Question 4 – Foundation*

(a) (i) Li; Be; C; N; O; F; Ne – symbol *or* name of any one of these. [1]
(ii) Be; Mg *or* name of **one** of these. [1]

(b) (i) Cl [1] gas [1] green [1]
(ii) Bleaching or sterilising water; or making PVC; or making hydrochloric acid – any **one** of these. [1]
(iii) They have the same outer electron arrangement [1] – seven outer shell /energy level electrons [1].

(c) **M** is lithium, Li (atomic number 3) [1]; **Z** is sulphur, S (atomic number 16) [1].

(d) Noble gas atoms give full outer shells/energy levels [1] so they cannot transfer or share electrons.

**Total: 11 marks**

### *Question 5 – Student answer*

(a) (i) Solid ✓

***Examiner's note*** Good, melting point and boiling point rise down the group.

(ii) Chlorine ✓

***Examiner's note*** Yes, most reactive at the top of the group for halogens.

(iii) Chlorine poisons bacteria ✓ as well as humans but is added to water at too small a dose to kill humans.

***Examiner's note*** More precisely, the toxic dose is related to the weight of the organism. Humans weigh more than bacteria!

(b) Hydrogen 1
Chlorine 2 8 7 ✓
Sodium 2 8 1 ✓

***Examiner's note*** No problems here. You must get all three correct for two marks.

(c) (i)

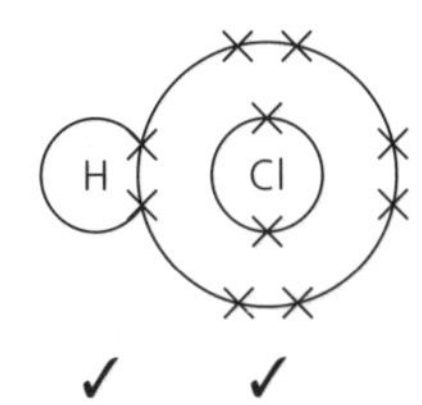


*Figure A2.2*

✓ ✓

***Examiner's note*** Good, it is wise to put in all the electrons unless you are asked for the outer shells only.

(ii)

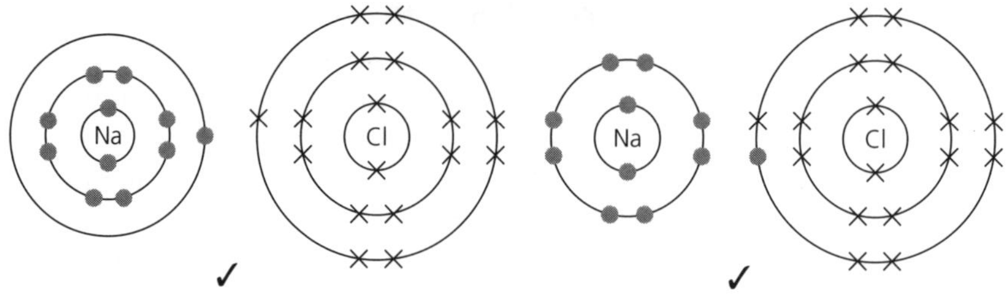

Figure A2.3

Na Cl Na Cl

| 2, 8, 1 | + ✓ | 2, 8, 7 | → | 2, 8(+) | + ✓ | 2, 8, 8(−) |
|---|---|---|---|---|---|---|

***Examiner's note*** Very good. You have shown both the structure and the transfer of the single electron. An alternative would have been to give the electronic structures as shown above.

(d) *Sodium chloride is a giant structure ✓ because it is composed of ions ✓ and not molecules.*

***Examiner's note*** A good answer. Molecular structures have covalent bonding.

Full marks, Well done! This is A* quality.

**Total: 13 marks**

# 3 *Solutions* **Organic Chemistry**

## SOLUTIONS TO REVISION ACTIVITIES

**1** (a) hydrocarbon (b) unsaturated (c) cracking (d) salt (e) addition.

**2** (a) butane (b) propene (c) methanol (d) methanoic acid.

**3** (a) $CH_4$ (b) $C_2H_4$ (c) $C_3H_7OH$ (d) $CH_3CO_2H$.

**4** (a) ethane and propane (b) butene, ethane, poly(styrene) and propane (c) ethene (d) poly(styrene) (e) ethanol (f) sugar (g) methanoic acid.

**5** (a) isomers

(b) (i)

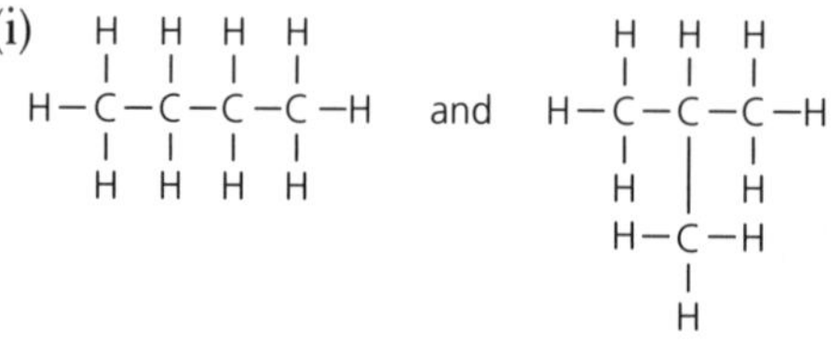

Figure A3.1

```
  H H H H               H H H
  | | | |               | | |
H-C-C-C-C-H    and    H-C-C-C-H
  | | | |               | | |
  H H H H               H | H
                      H-C-H
                          |
                          H
```

(ii)

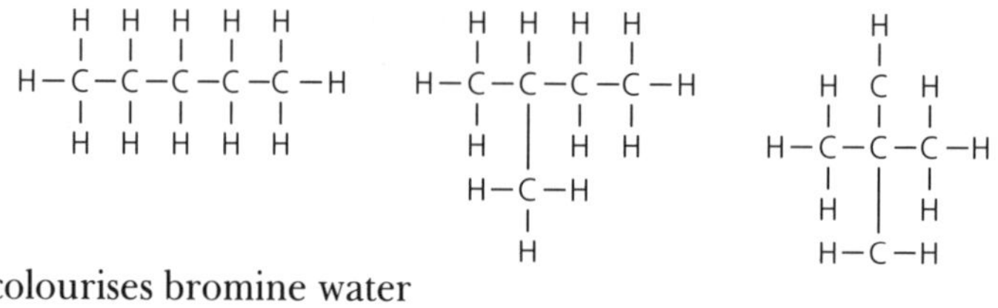

Figure A3.2

```
  H H H H H           H H H H                 H
  | | | | |           | | | |                 |
H-C-C-C-C-C-H       H-C-C-C-C-H             H C H
  | | | | |           | | | |               | | |
  H H H H H           H | H H             H-C-C-C-H
                    H-C-H                   | | |
                      |                     H | H
                      H                   H-C-H
```

**6** (a) decolourises bromine water

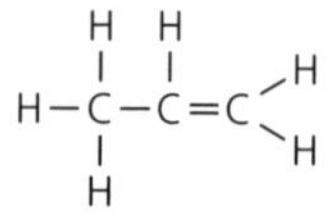

Figure A3.3

(b)

```
  H H
  | |  H
H-C-C=C<
  |    H
  H
```

The **double bond** is unsaturated.

(c) (i) propanol (ii) poly(propene)

**7** (a) fractional distillation

(b) any **three** from: petrol (fuel for car); paraffin (fuel for aircraft and oil stoves); diesel oil (fuel for diesel engines); lubricating oil (lubricant); fuel oil (heating fuel).

(c) cracking – large molecules are made into more useful smaller molecules.

**8** (a) sodium stearate (b) saponification (c) ester

(d) soap insoluble in salt solution

## SOLUTIONS TO PRACTICE QUESTIONS

### *Question 1 – Foundation*

(a) (i) A compound containing carbon and hydrogen only. [1]
(ii) Crude oil/natural gas. [1]

(b) **Two from**: compounds in it have a general formula; similar chemical properties; graded physical properties.

(c) 18. [1]

**Total: 5 marks**

### *Question 2 – Foundation and Higher*

*Figure A3.4a* (a) (i) 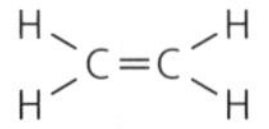 $H_2C=CH_2$ [1]

poly(propene) [1]

*Figure A3.4b* $-[CF_2-CF_2]_n-$ [1]

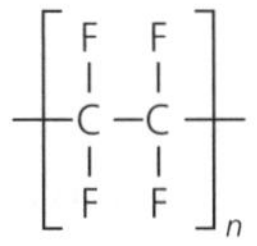

(ii) Ethene/propene. [1]
(iii) All contain a double bond. [1]
(iv) $C_2F_4$ [1]
(v) Any sensible suggestion such as when a non-conductor is required or where the density has to be low. [1]

(b) (i) Leave in water until all other materials sink. [1]
(ii) Use a magnet. [1]

**Total: 9 marks**

### *Question 3 – Student answer*

(a) (i) liquid gas ✓ [1/1]
(ii) Unsaturated means it has lost atoms. Saturated means it is 'full up' with atoms ✗ [0/1]

***Examiner's note*** This is too vague an unsaturated hydrocarbon contains a double bond.

(b) (i) Ethene joins with other ethene molecules to form a longer molecule. [1/2]

***Examiner's note*** Probably worth one mark only. It is a reaction in which a number of small unsaturated molecules add to each other to form a large molecule.

(ii) $C_2H_4\,(g) + C_8H_{18}\,(l) \rightarrow C_{10}H_{22}(l)$ ✗ [0/2]

***Examiner's note*** This is not polymerisation. The correct equation should be $n(C_2H_4) \rightarrow -(CH_2H_2C)_n-$

(iii) plastic carrier bags ✓ [1/1]

(c) (i) Plastic B. ✓ Reason Very flexible. ✓ [2/2]
(ii) Plastic C. ✓ Reason transparent so you can see your fish. ✓ [2/2]

***Examiner's note*** The student has scored 7/11, which would give a grade C/B. The answer could have been improved by learning definitions at the beginning of this chapter.

# 4 Solutions
# Industrial Chemistry and electrolysis

## SOLUTIONS TO REVISION ACTIVITIES

**1** (a) ores
(b) pure
(c) reduction
(d) haematite; carbon (coke)
(e) electrolysis or electrolytic reduction
(f) cryolite; cathode
(g) decomposition; direct electric current
(h) $Cu^{2+}$; Cu
(i) nitrogen; hydrogen; 450 °C; 200 atmospheres; iron
(j) nitric acid

**2** (a) sulphur; oxygen(air); sulphur dioxide
(b) sulphur trioxide; 450 °C; vanadium; oxide.
(c) oleum; 98 %.

**3** Limestone is decomposed by heating to 1000 ° C in natural gas-heated kilns.

$$\underset{\text{calcium carbonate}}{CaCO_3} \rightarrow \underset{\text{calcium oxide}}{CaO} + \underset{\text{carbon dioxide}}{CO_2}$$

**4** (a) aircraft parts; overhead power lines
(b) car bodies; washing machine bodies
(c) household electrical wiring; water tanks
(d) making ammonium nitrate fertiliser; manufacture of nitric acid
(e) car-battery electrolyte; making detergents
(f) making ammonium nitrate fertiliser; making explosives
(g) agricultural use to cure acidity in soils; mixed with sand, cement and water to make mortar
(h) as a sterilising agent for domestic water supplies; making PVC plastic
(i) making anti-knock for leaded petrol; making medicinal drugs
(j) making soap; making paper

**5** (a) An ore is a mixture of minerals containing economically extractable quantities of an element, e.g. haematite or bauxite
(b) Reduction is the removal of oxygen from a compound,e.g. the reduction of iron (III) oxide to iron using carbon
(c) exothermic reactions give out heat, e.g. $C + O_2 \rightarrow CO_2$
(d) endothermic reactions take in heat, e.g. $CO_2 + C \rightarrow 2CO$
(e) a reaction comes to equilibrium when the rate of the forward and backward reactions are the same, e.g. $N_2 + 3H_2 \rightleftarrows 2NH_3$
(f) a nitrogenous fertiliser is one that supplies a plant with combined nitrogen, e.g. ammonium nitrate
(g) alloy steels are solid mixtures of iron with (usually) transition metals, e.g. manganese steel or vanadium steel
(h) cathodic reduction is the gain of electrons by an atom or ion at the cathode in electrolysis, e.g. $Na^+ + e^- \rightarrow Na$
(i) anodic oxidation is the loss of electrons by an atom or ion at the anode during electrolysis, e.g $2Cl^- \rightarrow Cl_2 + 2e^-$
(j) A catalyst is a substance that speeds up a chemical reaction and is unchanged at the end of the process, e.g vanadium (V) oxide in the Contact process.

## SOLUTIONS TO PRACTICE QUESTIONS

### *Question 1 – Higher*

(a) (i) natural gas [1] and water [1].
(ii) Carbon dioxide is an acidic oxide so will be converted to a salt by the alkali. [1]

(b) (i) 1; 3; and 2. All must be correct for [1].
(ii) It is the sign for a **reversible reaction** or an **equilibrium sign** [1].
(iii) Increased pressure means more molecules per unit volume (or increased concentration) [1] which leads to an increased number of collisions per second [1].
(iv) Catalysts speed up reactions so giving more product per unit of time [1] but the catalyst is not used up and so its cost is fixed [1]. The reaction can be carried out at a lower pressure and/or temperature [1].

### *Question 2 – Higher*

(a) (i) Electrolysis is decomposition [1] of a substance by passage of a direct electric current [1].
(ii) Cathode [1].
(iii) Bubbles/gas [1) green/yellow colour [1] distinctive 'bleach'/'chlorine' smell [1].
(iv) Bubbles/gas [1]; colourless [1].
(v) $2H^+ + 2e \rightarrow H_2$; or $2H_2O + 2e^- \rightarrow H_2 + 2OH^-$ [2]

(b) (i) The anode is made of impure copper [1]. The cathode is a thin sheet of pure copper [1]. The electrolyte is copper sulphate solution [1]. Electrolysis dissolves the copper off the anode [1] and deposits pure copper on the cathode [1].
(ii) $Cu^{2+} + 2e^- \rightarrow Cu$

## Section B questions

In the answers to Questions 3 and 4 in Section B below, the marking points are underlined.

### *Question 3 – Foundation*

Sulphur is burnt in air to give sulphur dioxide:

$S + O_2 \rightarrow SO_2$

The gas is passed with excess air over a vanadium(v) oxide catalyst at 450 °C and forms sulphur trioxide:

$2SO_2 + O_2 \rightleftarrows 2SO_3$

Sulphur trioxide is then dissolved in concentrated sulphuric acid to make 'oleum':

$SO_3 + H_2SO_4 \rightarrow H_2S_2O_7$

which is then diluted with water to the final 98% sulphuric acid:

$H_2S_2O_7 + H_2O \rightarrow 2H_2SO_4$

**Maximum marks 10**

### *Question 4 – Higher*

(a) Impure molten iron is taken from the blast furnace in large metal containers called converters. Oxygen is blown through the molten iron and this removes the carbon impurity which burns or is oxidised to carbon dioxide /carbon monoxide which escapes from the top of the converter.

$C + O_2 \rightarrow CO_2$ **OR** $2C + O_2 \rightarrow 2CO$

The impurity removed is carbon. This makes the steel not so brittle and easier to shape.

**Maximum marks 7**

(b) Alloy steels are steels with extra elements for special properties, for example manganese in steels gives extra hardness. Manganese steel is used in railway lines at crossings.

**Maximum marks 3**

***Question 5 – Higher***

(a) Aluminium oxide/alumina [1], **not bauxite**, which is the ore itself.
(b) To lower the melting point of the aluminium oxide/to dissolve the aluminium oxide [1]; to allow conduction to take place [1].
(c) Electrolysis can only occur when ions can move [1], i.e. in the molten state or in solution [1].
(d) Cathode/negative electrode. [1]
(e) $Al^{3+} + 3e^- \rightarrow Al$ [2]
(f) Carbon [1] anodes react with the oxygen [1] discharged at the anode to form carbon monoxide/carbon dioxide [1].
(g) Two uses [2] *with* reasons [2] from the following: aircraft bodies (LD/ST); drinks cans (LD); pans (HC); foil (HC/HR); overhead power lines (EC/LD).
Reasons given in bracketed codes: low density/weight (LD); good heat conduction (HC); heat resistance (HR); good electrical conduction (EC); strong for the weight (ST).

***Question 6 – Student answer***

(a) (i) An ore is the rock that a metal is extracted from.. ✓ [1/1]
(ii) Coke, limestone, iron ore and ✓✗ [1/2]

***Examiner's note*** The one you couldn't get is air – so only 1/2 marks because the other raw materials are given!

(b) (i) It is a reduction reaction. ✓ [1/1]
(ii) The iron oxide is converted to iron which is reduction. ✗ [0/1]

***Examiner's note*** True, but not the explanation. It is reduction because oxygen is removed from the oxide.

(iii) To make the reduction process easier. ✗ [0/1]

***Examiner's note*** A bit lame as I'm sure you realised. Limestone reacts with acidic impurities converting them to slag.

(c) (i) Medium steel. ✓ [1/1]
(ii) Saws have teeth that must be hard and they must not break. ✓ [1/1]

***Examiner's note*** Good answers to (c) (i) and (ii). Hard teeth retain their sharpness. Also saws need to bend a little.

Score = 5/8 A reasonably good answer – about grade C quality.

# 5 Solutions
# ***Aqueous Chemistry – acids, bases and salts***

## SOLUTIONS TO REVISION ACTIVITIES

**1** (a) hydrogen or hydroxonium (b) hydroxide or hydroxyl
(c) neutralise; salt; water (d) partially (e) soluble or water soluble

**2** (a) Any **three** of: hydrochloric, nitric, sulphuric, ethanoic, citric, tartaric.
(b) Any **three** of: sodium hydroxide, potassium hydroxide, calcium hydroxide and ammonia solution/ammonium hydroxide.

(c) Any **three** metal oxides other than those of the Alkali metals.

3 (i) Method b (ii) Method c (iii) Method a.

4 (a) violet (b) blue (c) orange-yellow.

5 (a) $HCl + H_2O \rightarrow H_3O^+ + Cl^-$ **or** $HCl + aq \rightarrow H^+ + Cl^-$

(b) $CH_3CO_2H + H_2O \rightleftarrows CH_3CO_2^- + H_3O^+$ **or**
$CH_3CO_2H + aq \rightleftarrows CH_3CO_2^- + H^+$

6
- ▶ calcium carbonate (S)
- ▶ sodium hydroxide solution (ALK)
- ▶ copper (II) oxide (B)
- ▶ ammonia solution (ALK)

7 (a) A white precipitate. (b) A dirty-green precipitate.
(c) A pale blue precipitate.

8
- ▶ sodium chloride (S).
- ▶ ammonium sulphate (S)
- ▶ silver chloride (IS)
- ▶ calcium nitrate (S)

9 (a) This is vinegar – a condiment, for pickling, for defurring kettles.
(b) Agriculture – to raise the pH of soil or mixed with cement, sand and water to make mortar.
(c) Car battery acid.
(d) This is commonly known as bicarbonate of soda used in indigestion tablets or as a raising agent in cake-mixes.
(e) Neutralises bee or jellyfish stings.

## SOLUTIONS TO PRACTICE QUESTIONS

***Question 1 – Foundation***

(a) (i) It is an acid **or** it is acidic [1].
(ii) 7 [1].

(b) (i) Dilute acids have smaller amounts [1] of pure acid in the same volume of solution [1]; **or** dilute acids have larger volumes of water [1] for the same amount of the pure acid [1].
(ii) Add an alkali [1] dropwise until indicator becomes green [1].

(c) (i) The diagram should show filter paper [1]; a collecting vessel [1]; solid residue on the filter paper (say in black shading) [1].
(ii) Limewater (calcium hydroxide solution) [1]; goes milky [1].
(iii) Copper sulphate [1]; carbon dioxide [1]; water [1].
(iv) Copper(II) oxide or copper(II) hydroxide [1].

***Question 2 – Higher***

(a) Sodium [1]
(b) Neutralisation [1]
(c) (i) Green [1] (ii) 3 – 4 [1]
(d) pH would rise [1]
(e) (i) $H^+$ or $H_3O^+$ [1] (ii) $OH^-$ [1]
(iii) $H^+ + OH^- \rightarrow H_2O$ or $H_3O^+ + OH^- \rightarrow 2H_2O$ [1]

***Question 3 – Higher/Foundation***

(a) Sample **R** [1].
(b) Sample **P** [1].
(c) Sample **P** is the only sample containing sulphate ions and no chloride ions [1].
(d) Sample **S** [1] (it contains none of the ions tested for).

***Question 4 – Foundation***

(a) pH 7 [1] (neutral).
(b) Sodium chloride solution [1].
(c) Sodium hydroxide solution [1].
1. Sodium carbonate. Use: glass making/water softening. [1]
2. Sodium hydroxide. Use: soap making/paper making. [1]

**Total: 5 marks**

***Question 5 – Student answer***

(a) (i) They don't react all that well with water and they have a low pH. ✓ [1/2]

**Examiner's note** Worth 1 mark, weak acids do not completely ionise in water; some of the molecules of tartaric acid are not ionised in water.

(ii) Name of acid tartaric.
Reason it has a higher pH than sulphuric and also it ✓ reacts slower. [1/2]

(b) (i) I would pipette 25 $cm^3$ of the white wine into a flask. ✓ Then I would add the sodium hydroxide ✓ solution from a burette. ✓ When the indicator (phenolpthalien) ✓ turned pink ✓ I would stop. I would know the volume of alkali used by taking the reading from the burette. ✓ I would have started at zero. [7/7]

**Examiner's note** An excellent answer – full marks.

(ii) Red wine is the same colour as phenolphthalein and the indicator would not work ✓ [1/1]

(c) (i) $\frac{25 \times X}{1000}$ moles of acid $= \frac{20 \times 0.1}{2 \times 1000}$ moles of alkali ✗

So $X = \frac{1000 \times 20 \times 0.1}{25 \times 1000}$ ✓

$X = \frac{2000}{25\,000} = 0.8$ moles per litre ✓ [2/3]

**Examiner's note** A fair attempt: However, you did not take the equation into account. Each mole of acid reacts with **2 moles of the alkali**. This means that the acid has twice as much neutralising power as the number of moles would suggest, so its concentration is only 0.04 moles **per litre** – 2 marks out of 3.

(ii) Its a weak acid so would have less concentration. ✗ [0/1]

**Examiner's note** Unfortunately not so. A weak acid does not neutralise less alkali than a strong acid of the same concentration. The answer is that there are probably other acids present in wine – like acetic acid (ethanoic).

Overall a good answer worth 12/15 and at higher level an A grade.

# 6 *Solutions* ***How far, how fast and energetics***

## SOLUTIONS TO REVISION ACTIVITIES

1 (a) equilibrium (b) catalyst (c) enzymes (d) exothermic (e) water.

2 (a) You should have labelled the catalyst, the hydrogen peroxide solution and the syringe (see Figure 6.2).
(b) Any transition metal oxide copper(II) oxide, chromium(III) oxide, manganese(IV) oxide.
(c) $2H_2O_2(aq) \rightarrow 2H_2O(l) + O_2(g)$
(d) Add anhydrous copper(II) sulphate – colour changes from white to blue.
(e) Re-lights a glowing splint.
(f) A
(g) The reaction has finished, the hydrogen peroxide has completely decomposed.

(h) Use more finely divided catalyst; heat the hydrogen peroxide.

**4** (a) (i) $2H_2(g) + O_2(g) \rightarrow 2H_2O(l)$ (ii) endothermic (iii) O–H

(b) Heat, light, sound.

## SOLUTIONS TO PRACTICE QUESTIONS

***Question 1 – Foundation***

(a) To increase the rate of reaction [1] and give a good yield in a short time [1].

(b) The heat liberated is used for other purposes [1], e.g. to produce electricity for the site [1].

**Total: 4 marks**

***Question 2 – Higher***

(a) Carbon dioxide. [1]

(b) (i) Graph fits graph paper, i.e. sensible scale [1]; units given on axis [1]; correct points plotted [1]; smooth curve [1]

(ii) Reading from graph (either 47, 48 or 49 seconds). [1]

(iii) No more bubbles. [1]

(iv) Marble chips remained. [1]

(v) $50\,cm^3$ (units **must** be given). [1]

(c) (i) More quickly. [1]

(ii) Either more marble *or* more surface area [1].

(iii) Steeper at start [1] same final volume [1].

**Total: 13 marks**

***Question 3 – Higher***

(a) Reasonable scale chosen [1]; axes labelled [1]; all plots correct [1]; smooth curve [1].

(b) Curve with less steep gradient [1], maximum volume $25\,cm^3$ [1].

(c) Number of $H_2O_2$ particles are reduced as it breaks down into water and oxygen [1] less chance of collisions [1] with catalyst [1].

(d) Increases number of collisions between reactants per unit time [1]. More energy [1] to break/form bonds [1].

(e) (i) Exothermic [1]. 65.1 kJ of energy released [1].

(ii) More energy [1] given out in forming new bonds [1] than taken in breaking bonds [1].

**Total: 17 marks**

***Question 4 – Student answer***

(a) It acts as a catalyst ✓ [1/1]

(b) (i) The yield decreases ✓ [1/1]

(ii) The yield increases ✓ [1/1]

(c) As the temperature increases the particles gain more energy but they do not get the opportunity to collide with other particles because they are moving too fast. ✗ [0/3]

***Examiner's note*** You have completely the wrong idea here! The particles will move faster, collide more frequently and thus increase the chance of successful collisions.

(d) Heat energy is taken in to help form the molecules ✗ [0/1]

***Examiner's note*** The reaction goes faster at a higher temperature.

This is a very poor answer on a higher paper (3/7). If the rest of the answers on your examination paper were like this you would have been ungraded. You ought to consider taking the foundation paper.

# 7 Solutions
# Metals, non-metals and compounds

## SOLUTIONS TO REVISION ACTIVITIES

**1** (a) malleable (b) basic (c) hydrogen
(d) non-metals (e) noble/inert (f) allotropes
**2** (a) potassium calcium zinc lead copper
(b) calcium and potassium (c) copper
(d) brown precipitate of copper, solution will turn from blue to colourless
(e) potassium (f) potassium
**3** (a) fluorine chlorine oxygen bromine iodide sulphur (b) bromine
(c) oxygen and sulphur (d) oxygen (e) sulphur (f) bromine
**4** (a) magnesium and oxygen to give magnesium oxide
(b) carbon oxidised by oxygen to form carbon dioxide
(c) zinc plus copper sulphate gives copper plus zinc sulphate
(d) chlorine plus hydrogen forming hydrogen chloride
(e) nitrogen + hydrogen $\rightleftarrows$ ammonia

## SOLUTIONS TO PRACTICE QUESTIONS

### *Question 1 – Foundation*

(a) **C** [1] and **E** [1] (b) **E** [1] (c) **A** [1] **B** [1]
(d) Evaporation/crystallisation. [1]

**Total: 6 marks**

### *Question 2 – Higher*

(a) (i) Chromium would burn [1] in oxygen to forms its oxide [1].
(ii) No reaction [1].
(iii) Chromium would react [1] with the acid to give hydrogen [1].
(b) Gold is very unreactive/does not react with [1] water/acids/food/oxygen/air [1].
(c) calcium + water → calcium hydroxide + hydrogen [1]
(d) $Zn + H_2O \rightarrow ZnO + H_2$. If the symbols are correct [1] and if the equation is balanced [1].
(e) The magnesium ribbon would become coated [1] with a pink/red-brown/brown solid [1]. Or, Magnesium dissolves: copper deposit forms.
(f) Copper [1] as it does not react with steam [1]. Magnesium and iron would react with steam [1].

**Total: 15 marks**

### *Question 3 – Student answer*

(a) Most reactive C E A D B Least reactive [4/4]

***Examiner's note*** Well done, this is the correct order.

(b) May cause explosive and dangerous reaction ✓ [1/1]

***Examiner's note*** Yes, reaction would be too violent.

(c) A = iron, B = gold, C = calcium, D = copper, E = magnesium. [1/1]

***Examiner's note*** You have identified the metals correctly.

(d) The particles are packed closely together, so heat can be conducted, as heat energy is passed on to each particle from another. Metals also contain electrons which conduct electricity as it passes from each electron to another. [0/3]

***Examiner's note*** This is too muddled to gain any marks. Metals have a giant structure in which electrons, from the highest energy levels, are free to move through the whole structure thus enabling the metal to conduct electricity. Heat causes atoms to vibrate; this vibration passes from atom to atom through the structure.

Score = 6/9, but you scored these on the Foundation questions. This would be equivalent to a C grade.

# 8 *Solutions* ***Quantitative Chemistry***

## SOLUTIONS TO REVISION ACTIVITIES

**1** (a) atomic (b) molecular (formula) (c) mole (d) Faraday
**2** (a) 80 (b) 246 (c) 88
**3** (a) 1 (b) 3 (c) 2
**4** $MnO_2$
**5** 1 (one) molar
**6** 3 (three) litres ($dm^3$)
**7** (a) 2 (b) 2 (c) 4 (d) 6 (e) 4

## SOLUTIONS TO PRACTICE QUESTIONS

### *Question 1 – Higher*

(a) (i) 3.2 g [1] (ii) $\frac{8.4}{56}$ of iron: $\frac{3.2}{16}$ of oxygen [1] (iii) $\frac{3}{2}$ : 2 [1] (iv) $Fe_3O_4$ [1]

(b) 56 g of iron give 63.5 g of copper [1]

14 tonnes of iron gives $\frac{63.5}{56} \times 14$ tonnes of copper [1] 15.9 tonnes [1]

**Total: 7 marks**

### *Question 2 – Higher*

(a) $\frac{5.27}{64}$ of Cu; $\frac{4.61}{56}$ of Fe; $\frac{5.27}{32}$ of S.

0.082 of Cu [1]; 0.082 of Fe [1] and 0.164 of S [1]

Ratio is 1:1:2, therefore formula is $CuFeS_2$ [1]

(b) (i) $2CuS + 3O_2 \rightarrow 2CuO + 2SO_2$

Formulae correct [1] balanced [1].

(ii) From the equation 1 mole of CuS (96 g) gives 1 mole of CuO (80 g) [1], hence 800 kg formed [1].

**Total: 8 marks**

### *Question 3 – Higher*

(a) (i) 0.05 [2] (ii) 0.05 [1] (iii) 1.2 litres [1] (iv) 4.05 g [2]

(b) Number of moles of ZnO reacted = 0.016 [1]

Mass of ZnO reacted = 1.296 g [1] Excess ZnO = 2.754 g [1]

**Total: 9 marks**

***Question 4 – Student answer***

(a) (i) NaCl 23 + 35.5. = 58.5 ✓ [1/3]

(ii) $CaCl_2$ 40 + (35.5 × 2) = 111 ✓ [1/3]

(iii) $C_6H_6$ (6 × 12) + (6 × 1) = 78 ✓ [1/3]

(iv) $CuSO_4.5H_2O$ (64 + 32 + (4 × 16).5(× 18) = 112 + 90 = 202 ✓ [1/3]

***Examiner's note*** Part (iv) is worth 1/3 for getting the water right. You have only added in one oxygen atom instead of 4; the correct answer was 160 + 90 = 250.

(b) (i) 4 × 80 = 120 ✗
439 – 120 = 319 [0/3]

***Examiner's note*** 4 × 80 = 320 not 120!! You should have realised you were wrong – no element has a relative atomic mass of 319. The answer should have been 119.

(ii) magnesium ✗ [0/1]

***Examiner's note*** This was a guess – the symbol for magnesium is Mg. Element 119 is tin.

You would have scored 4/10 which is equivalent to a grade G/F grade.

# 9 Solutions
# *The Earth and its atmosphere*

## SOLUTIONS TO REVISION ACTIVITIES

**1** (a) Any **two** of methane, ammonia, carbon monoxide and hydrogen sulphide.
(b) The surface cooled to 100 °C or below.
(c) 1. melting then crystallisation/solidification
2. sedimentary rock
3. heat and /or high pressure
(d) (i) slow cooling of magma (intrusion)
(ii) building/kerbstones
(iii) limestone/sandstone/coal/rock salt
(iv) sedimentation + lithification (compression + cementation)
(v) marble or slate
(vi) building or roofing

**2** Salts, leached from the land by rain, run into rivers and so to the sea.

**3** Earthquakes; volcanic.

**4** **A** is basalt/extrusive rock; **B** is granite/intrusive rock; **C** is magma.

**5** (a) The San Andreas Fault.
(b) The Mid-Atlantic Ridge.
(c) The West coast of South America – the Andes.

## SOLUTIONS TO PRACTICE QUESTIONS

***Question 1 – Higher***

(a)
- The Sun heats/evaporates water from the sea/ocean. [1]
- Water vapour cools as it rises [1]. Water vapour condenses as it cools. [1] Condensed water forms droplets and finally large drops which fall as rain. [1]
- Rainwater soaks through land to enter rivers and finally reaches the sea once more. [1]

(b) (i) Sedimentary.
(ii) 1. Igneous 2. Metamorphic 3. Sedimentary.
All correct – two marks; one correct – one mark.
(iii) Limestone is converted into marble at high temperature and high pressure [1]. These conditions destroy the fossils. [1]

***Question 2 –Higher***

(a) Igneous [1]
(b) E [1]
(c) The surface cools quicker than the middle [1] because it is cooled by the surrounding air. Faster cooling produces smaller crystals [1].
**OR** Cooling rate is slower [1] in the middle of the layer so crystals are larger [1].

***Question 3 – Higher***

(a) (i) New crust formation or volcanoes. [1]
(ii) They make the plates move apart [1] producing earthquakes at the other edge [1].
(b) Present-day continents formed by continental drift [1] through the motion of floating 'tectonic' plates [1]. In the future the plates will continue to move apart [1] changing the arrangement of the land masses [1].

***Question 4 – Student answer***

(a) They are composed of different minerals. ✓ [1/2]

***Examiner's note*** This looks like a guess, but gains one mark. Another difference arises from different proportions of the three minerals in granite.

(b) Granite has big crystals, basalt has small crystals. ✓ [1/2]

***Examiner's note*** Only one mark even though it looks like two points! Colour will vary also – with different proportions of the minerals.

(c) It was probably formed by extrusion of magma from the volcano. ✗
It is still there today because volcanic rock is hard. ✓ [1/2]

***Examiner's note*** Did you read the question? The rock is the intrusive core, not extrusive – it is granite, which is very resistant to weathering.

Score = 3/6. Half marks. On a higher level question this is grade C.

*part IV*

# Timed practice paper with answers

# Timed practice paper

**Time allowed:** 2 hours

***Question 1***

Chemists spend a great deal of time carrying out processes to make materials or finding uses for these materials. Some of these processes involve chemical changes, others physical changes.

For the processes below, put a (C) in the box for each chemical change, and a (P) for each physical change. The first one has been done for you.

(a) Making soap from vegetable oil and sodium hydroxide. [C]

(b) Taking 'antacids' to cure indigestion. [ ]

(c) Putting lime on soil to increase the pH. [ ]

(d) Making diamonds from graphite. [ ]

(e) Anodising aluminium. [ ]

(f) Compressed nitrogen gas propelling paint from a spray can. [ ]

**Total: 5 marks**

***Question 2***

Ammonium nitrate is used as a fertiliser.

The following word equations describe reactions by which ammonium nitrate is made.

Reaction 1 nitrogen + gas **A** $\leftrightharpoons$ gas **B**

Reaction 2 gas **B** + excess oxygen + liquid **C** $\rightarrow$ acid **D**

Reaction 3 gas **B** + acid **D** $\rightarrow$ ammonium nitrate

(a) Identify **A**, **B**, **C** and **D**.

**A** is ..........................................................

**B** is ..........................................................

**C** is ..........................................................

**D** is .......................................................... [4]

(b) Gas **A** is obtained from natural gas. What is the chemical name of natural gas?

.......................................................... [1]

(c) What are the conditions for Reaction 1?

Approximate temperature ..........................................................

Approximate pressure ..........................................................

Catalyst .......................................................... [3]

(d) Name two industrial processes other than Reaction 2 that use oxygen.

(i) ..........................................................

(ii) .......................................................... [2]

(e) Give two reasons why ammonium nitrate is such a good fertiliser.

. . . . . . . . . . . . . . . . . . . . . . . . . . . . . . . . . . . . . . . . . . . . . . . . . . . . . . . . . . . . . .

. . . . . . . . . . . . . . . . . . . . . . . . . . . . . . . . . . . . . . . . . . . . . . . . . . . . . . . . . . . . [2]

(f) What might happen if too much ammonium nitrate is added to the soil?

. . . . . . . . . . . . . . . . . . . . . . . . . . . . . . . . . . . . . . . . . . . . . . . . . . . . . . . . . . . . . .

. . . . . . . . . . . . . . . . . . . . . . . . . . . . . . . . . . . . . . . . . . . . . . . . . . . . . . . . . . . . . .

. . . . . . . . . . . . . . . . . . . . . . . . . . . . . . . . . . . . . . . . . . . . . . . . . . . . . . . . . . . . [2]

**Total: 14 marks**

***Question 3***

The diagram below shows the rock cycle.

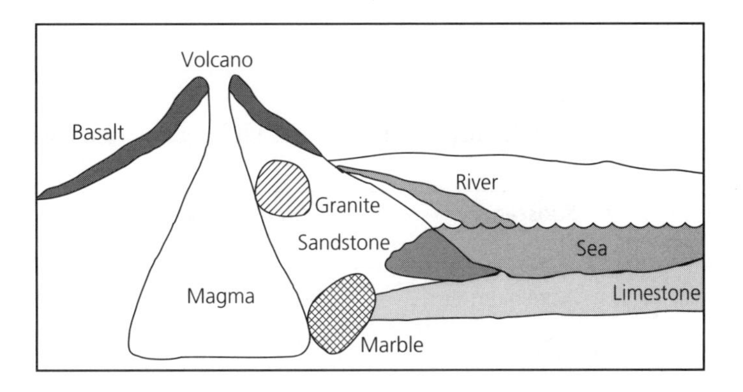


(a) Using the diagram above, complete the simplified diagram of the rock cycle below by inserting the ONE missing word in the box and the TWO missing arrow heads.

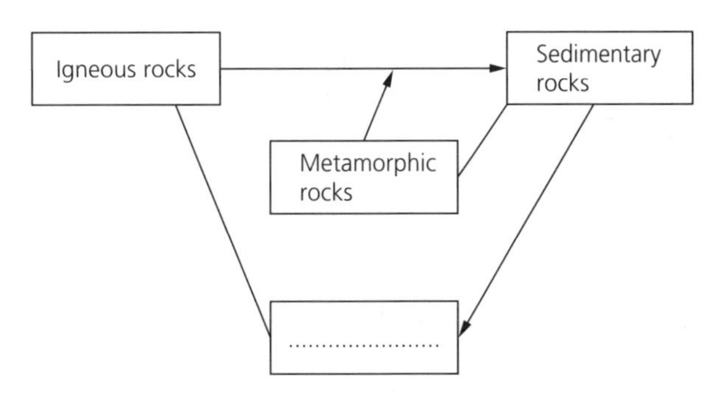


[3]

(b) Look at the top diagram and decide the rock type (igneous, metamorphic or sedimentary) for each of the following)

| *Rock sample* | *Rock type* |
|---|---|
| Basalt | |
| Granite | |
| Limestone | |
| Marble | |
| Sandstone | |

[5]

(c) Igneous rock can be changed into sedimentary rocks. Describe the processes that occur during this change.

..........................................................................

..........................................................................

..........................................................................

..........................................................................

.......................................................................... [4]

(d) In which type of rock would you expect to find fossils?

.......................................................................... [1]

**Total: 13 marks**

***Question 4***

Use the information in the table below to answer the following questions

| ***Substance*** | ***Melting point °C*** | ***Does the substance conduct electricity*** |
|---|---|---|
| Aluminium | 659 | Yes |
| Candle wax | 35–50 | No |
| Copper carbonate | Cannot be measured | No |
| Graphite | Sublimes at 4000 | Yes |
| Sodium | 98 | Yes |
| Tungsten | 3377 | Yes |

(a) (i) Which substance is a mixture?

..........................................................................

(ii) Explain the reason for your choice.

.......................................................................... [2]

(b) Graphite sublimes. What does this mean?

..........................................................................

..........................................................................

.......................................................................... [1]

(c) (i) Graphite is used as electrodes for electrolysis experiments. Apart from its ability to conduct electricity, what other property makes graphite suitable for making electrodes?

..........................................................................

(ii) Name a metal from the table that is manufactured from its oxide using graphite electrodes.

.......................................................................... [2]

(d) Why is tungsten used as the filament in electric light bulbs and not one of the other metals?

. . . . . . . . . . . . . . . . . . . . . . . . . . . . . . . . . . . . . . . . . . . . . . . . . . . . . . . . . . . .

. . . . . . . . . . . . . . . . . . . . . . . . . . . . . . . . . . . . . . . . . . . . . . . . . . . . . . . . . . . .

. . . . . . . . . . . . . . . . . . . . . . . . . . . . . . . . . . . . . . . . . . . . . . . . . . . . . . . . . . [1]

(e) Suggest why is it impossible to measure the melting point of copper carbonate

. . . . . . . . . . . . . . . . . . . . . . . . . . . . . . . . . . . . . . . . . . . . . . . . . . . . . . . . . . . .

. . . . . . . . . . . . . . . . . . . . . . . . . . . . . . . . . . . . . . . . . . . . . . . . . . . . . . . . . . . .

. . . . . . . . . . . . . . . . . . . . . . . . . . . . . . . . . . . . . . . . . . . . . . . . . . . . . . . . . . [1]

(f) Which substances would melt if placed in a container over boiling water?

. . . . . . . . . . . . . . . . . . . . . . . . . . . . . . . . . . . . . . . . . . . . . . . . . . . . . . . . . . [1]

**Total: 8 marks**

### *Question 5*

The equation for cracking ethane can be represented by either a chemical equation:

$C_2H_6(g) \rightarrow C_2H_4(g) + H_2(g)$

or a structural equation:

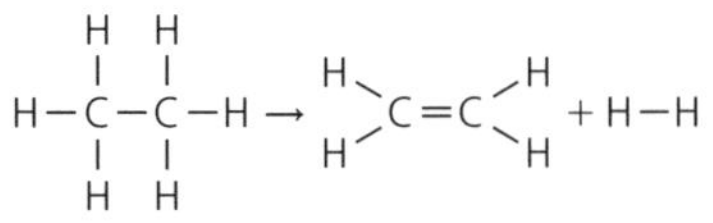

```
   H  H
   |  |         H       H
H—C—C—H  →      \C=C/      + H—H
   |  |         H/    \H
   H  H
```

(a) In a similar manner show the cracking of propane to propene and hydrogen.

Chemical equation . . . . . . . . . . . . . . . . . . . . . . . . . . . . . . . . . . . . . . . . . . . . . .

Structural equation

[3]

(b) Ethene undergoes addition polymerisation to poly(ethene).

(i) What is meant by an addition reaction?

. . . . . . . . . . . . . . . . . . . . . . . . . . . . . . . . . . . . . . . . . . . . . . . . . . . . . . . . . . . .

. . . . . . . . . . . . . . . . . . . . . . . . . . . . . . . . . . . . . . . . . . . . . . . . . . . . . . . . . . [1]

(ii) Write a full structural equation to show the formation of poly(ethene) from ethene.

[2]

(c) Give one use for poly(propene)

. . . . . . . . . . . . . . . . . . . . . . . . . . . . . . . . . . . . . . . . . . . . . . . . . . . . . . . . . . [1]

(d) Propane can also be cracked to form an alkene and an alkane. Write a symbol equation for this reaction

. . . . . . . . . . . . . . . . . . . . . . . . . . . . . . . . . . . . . . . . . . . . . . . . . . . . . . . . . . [1]

The table below gives various bond energies.

| *Bond* | *Energy kJ mol$^{-1}$* |
|---|---|
| C–C | 348 |
| C=C | 600 |
| C–H | 435 |
| H–H | 436 |

(e) Use data from the table to show that when ethane is cracked into ethene and hydrogen the energy change is + 182 kJ mol$^{-1}$.

[3]

(f) Draw the energy diagram for the cracking of ethane which is an endothermic reaction.

[1]

(g) The energy change when propane is cracked into propene and hydrogen is the same as that for cracking ethane to ethene and hydrogen. Comment on this fact. . . . . . . . . . . . . . . . . . . . . . . . . . . . . . . . . . . . . . . . . . . .

. . . . . . . . . . . . . . . . . . . . . . . . . . . . . . . . . . . . . . . . . . . . . . . . [2]

**Total: 14 marks**

***Question 6***

Sodium sulphate crystals $Na_2SO_4.10H_2O$ can be made by the following method.

Using a pipette place 50.00 cm$^3$ of 2.00 M sodium hydroxide solution into a conical flask and add three drops of methyl orange indicator. Add dilute sulphuric acid slowly until the indicator just turns red. Note the volume of sulphuric acid used (**62.50 cm$^3$**). Discard this solution.

Mix together **50.00 cm$^3$** of the **2.00 M** sodium hydroxide and **62.50 cm$^3$** of sulphuric acid (but do not add the indicator). Heat the solution of sodium sulphate until the volume is about one-third of its original volume. Leave the solution to cool. Filter off the crystals formed and dry between pieces of filter paper. Weigh the crystals (**3.30 grams**).

Weigh the saturated solution which is the filtrate ( **32.80 grams**)

**The figures in brackets were obtained for an actual experiment.**

(a) (i) What apparatus would be used to add the acid to the alkali?

. . . . . . . . . . . . . . . . . . . . . . . . . . . . . . . . . . . . . . . . . . . . . . . .

(ii) Why was the first solution thrown away and not used to prepare the sodium sulphate crystals?

. . . . . . . . . . . . . . . . . . . . . . . . . . . . . . . . . . . . . . . . . . . . . . . .

. . . . . . . . . . . . . . . . . . . . . . . . . . . . . . . . . . . . . . . . . . . . . . . . [2]

(b) Why are the crystals dried between filter papers and not heated with a Bunsen flame? . . . . . . . . . . . . . . . . . . . . . . . . . . . . . . . . . . . . . .

. . . . . . . . . . . . . . . . . . . . . . . . . . . . . . . . . . . . . . . . . . . . . . . . [1]

(c) The equation for the reaction is:

$2NaOH(aq) + H_2SO_4(aq) \rightarrow Na_2SO_4(aq) + 2H_2O(l)$

(i) Calculate the number of moles of sodium hydroxide in 50.0 $cm^3$ of 2.0 M solution.

(ii) Calculate the relative formula mass of $Na_2SO_4 \cdot 10H_2O$ and hence show that the maximum mass of the compound that could be formed is 16.1 g.

(iii) Calculate the number of moles of sulphuric acid in 62.5 $cm^3$ of solution and hence work out the molarity of the sulphuric acid.

[6]

(d) Why is the mass of crystals actually formed less than the value given in (c) (ii)?

. . . . . . . . . . . . . . . . . . . . . . . . . . . . . . . . . . . . . . . . . . . . . . . . . . . . . . . . . . . .

. . . . . . . . . . . . . . . . . . . . . . . . . . . . . . . . . . . . . . . . . . . . . . . . . . . . . . . . . . . . [1]

The solubility of a substance can be defined as the maximum mass of a substance that can be dissolved in 100 g of saturated solution at a given temperature.

(e) (i) Why is it necessary to quote temperature when quoting solubility?

. . . . . . . . . . . . . . . . . . . . . . . . . . . . . . . . . . . . . . . . . . . . . . . . . . . . . . . . . .

. . . . . . . . . . . . . . . . . . . . . . . . . . . . . . . . . . . . . . . . . . . . . . . . . . . . . . . . . .

(ii) Use this definition to work out the solubility of sodium sulphate crystals from the data collected in this experiment.

[4]

(f) If 25.00 $cm^3$ of sodium hydroxide and 62.50 $cm^3$ of sulphuric acid had been used, a different salt would have been formed. Suggest the name of this salt and write its formula.

Name . . . . . . . . . . . . . . . . . . . . . . . . . . . . . . . . . . . . . . . . . . . . . . . . . . . . . . . .

Formula . . . . . . . . . . . . . . . . . . . . . . . . . . . . . . . . . . . . . . . . . . . . . . . . . . . [2]

(g) Suggest why is it impossible to make magnesium sulphate crystals $MgSO_4.7H_2O$ by this method?

. . . . . . . . . . . . . . . . . . . . . . . . . . . . . . . . . . . . . . . . . . . . . . . . . . . . . . . . . . . . [1]

**Total: 17 marks**

### *Question 7*

Germanium is element number of 32 in the Periodic Table. It has a relative atomic mass of 73.

(a) (i) How many neutrons are there in one atom of germanium?

. . . . . . . . . . . . . . . . . . . . . . . . . . . . . . . . . . . . . . . . . . . . . . . . . . . . . . . . .

(ii) How many electrons are there in the outermost shell of a germanium atom. . . . . . . . . . . . . . . . . . . . . . . . . . . . . . . . . . . . . . . . . . . . . . . . . . . .

(iii) Explain how you arrived at your answer to (a) (ii).

. . . . . . . . . . . . . . . . . . . . . . . . . . . . . . . . . . . . . . . . . . . . . . . . . . . . . . . .

. . . . . . . . . . . . . . . . . . . . . . . . . . . . . . . . . . . . . . . . . . . . . . . . . . . . . . . .

(iv) Draw the structure of a molecule of germanium tetrachloride showing the outer (valency) electrons only.

[6]

(b) Germanium oxide melts at 1116 °C. The molten substance does not conduct electricity.

(i) From the position of germanium in the Periodic Table predict, with reasons, the type of oxide you think it will be (acidic, amphoteric, basic or neutral).

. . . . . . . . . . . . . . . . . . . . . . . . . . . . . . . . . . . . . . . . . . . . . . . . . . . . . . . .

. . . . . . . . . . . . . . . . . . . . . . . . . . . . . . . . . . . . . . . . . . . . . . . . . . . . . . . .

(ii) From the information given, predict the structure of germanium oxide.

. . . . . . . . . . . . . . . . . . . . . . . . . . . . . . . . . . . . . . . . . . . . . . . . . . . . . . . .

. . . . . . . . . . . . . . . . . . . . . . . . . . . . . . . . . . . . . . . . . . . . . . . . . . . . . [4]

(c) Germanium forms an homologous series of hydrides similar to the alkanes.

(i) Write down the general formula for the hydrides of germanium.

. . . . . . . . . . . . . . . . . . . . . . . . . . . . . . . . . . . . . . . . . . . . . . . . . . . . . . . .

(ii) Calculate the percentage of germanium in a hydride from this homologous series containing two germanium atoms.

[4]

**Total: 14 marks**

***Question 8***

Experiments were carried out on the rate of reaction of zinc with dilute sulphuric acid. In each experiment, excess sulphuric acid was used. The results are shown on the following graphs. In Experiment 1, 0.26 grams of powdered zinc were used. All three experiments were carried out at room temperature.

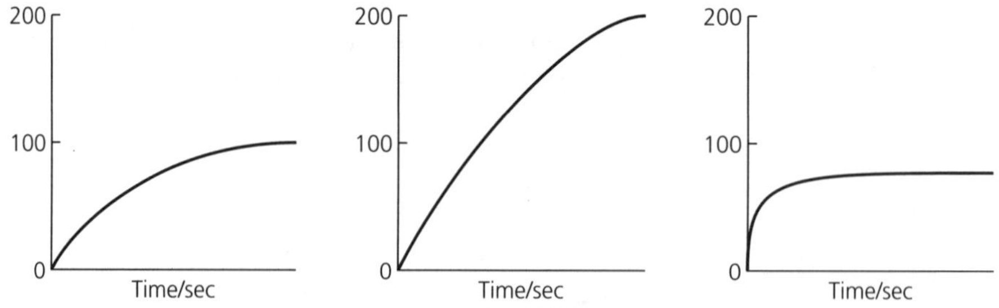


Experiment 1 | Experiment 2 | Experiment 3

(a) Write the symbol equation, including state symbols, for the reaction between zinc and dilute sulphuric acid.

. . . . . . . . . . . . . . . . . . . . . . . . . . . . . . . . . . . . . . . . . . . . . . . . . . . . . [2]

(b) The $x$-axis has been labelled for you. Suggest the label for the $y$-axis.

. . . . . . . . . . . . . . . . . . . . . . . . . . . . . . . . . . . . . . . . . . . . . . . . . . . . . [3]

(c) Suggest how the conditions might have been altered to produce the results for Experiment 2.

. . . . . . . . . . . . . . . . . . . . . . . . . . . . . . . . . . . . . . . . . . . . . . . . . . . . . . .

. . . . . . . . . . . . . . . . . . . . . . . . . . . . . . . . . . . . . . . . . . . . . . . . . . . . . [2]

(d) In Experiment 3 some copper(II) sulphate was added. Suggest reasons for the results obtained for this experiment.

. . . . . . . . . . . . . . . . . . . . . . . . . . . . . . . . . . . . . . . . . . . . . . . . . . . . . . .

. . . . . . . . . . . . . . . . . . . . . . . . . . . . . . . . . . . . . . . . . . . . . . . . . . . . . . .

. . . . . . . . . . . . . . . . . . . . . . . . . . . . . . . . . . . . . . . . . . . . . . . . . . . . . [2]

(e) Pure zinc is obtained by electrolysing zinc sulphate solution ($ZnSO_4$). Write the half equation for the discharge of zinc ions.

. . . . . . . . . . . . . . . . . . . . . . . . . . . . . . . . . . . . . . . . . . . . . . . . . . . . . [1]

Zinc is used as an ingredient in various alloys.

(f) (i) What is meant by an alloy?

. . . . . . . . . . . . . . . . . . . . . . . . . . . . . . . . . . . . . . . . . . . . . . . . . . .

(ii) Name a common alloy that contains zinc.

. . . . . . . . . . . . . . . . . . . . . . . . . . . . . . . . . . . . . . . . . . . . . . . . . [2]

(g) Explain why attaching a piece of zinc to an iron pipe prevents the pipe from rusting. . . . . . . . . . . . . . . . . . . . . . . . . . . . . . . . . . . . . . . . . . . . . . .

. . . . . . . . . . . . . . . . . . . . . . . . . . . . . . . . . . . . . . . . . . . . . . . . . . . . . . .

. . . . . . . . . . . . . . . . . . . . . . . . . . . . . . . . . . . . . . . . . . . . . . . . . . . . . . .

. . . . . . . . . . . . . . . . . . . . . . . . . . . . . . . . . . . . . . . . . . . . . . . . . . . . . [3]

**Total: 15 marks**

# Solutions to timed practice paper

The marks are shown in brackets immediately after the answer to which they apply.

***Question 1***

(a) C (b) C (c) C (d) P (e) C (f) P

**Total: 7 marks**

***Question 2***

(a) **A** is hydrogen [1] **B** is ammonia [1] **C** is water [1] **D** is nitric acid [1].
(b) Methane. [1]
(c) Approximate temperature – 400–450 °C. [1]
Approximate pressure – 200 atmospheres. [1]
Catalyst – iron/freshly reduced iron. [1]
(d) (i) Pure oxygen is used in steel making. [1]
(ii) Oxygen from air is used in making sulphuric acid. [1]

(e) Ammonium nitrate is a good fertiliser because (i) it contains a high proportion of available nitrogen [1] and (ii) because it is readily soluble in water [1].
(f) Excess ammonium nitrate in the soil may dissolve in rainwater and be washed into streams, rivers and lakes [1] causing eutrophication [1].

**Total: 14 marks**

***Question 3***

(a) The missing word in the box is **Magma** [1]. The missing arrows should be placed as follows:
Sedimentary rock → metamorphic rock [1] and magma → igneous rock [1].
(b) The rock types are as follows: basalt is **igneous** [1]; granite is **igneous** [1]; limestone is **sedimentary** [1]; marble is **metamorphic** [1]; sandstone is **sedimentary** [1].
(c) Igneous rock is weathered and eroded [1] then transported by wind, water or ice [1] to a sea or lake [1]. There it compacts and cements [1] forming sedimentary rock.
(d) Fossils are found only in sedimentary rock. [1]

**Total: 13 marks**

***Question 4***

(a) (i) Candle wax is a mixture [1] (ii) It melts over a range of temperatures [1].
(b) At 4000 °C solid graphite vaporises without melting. [1]
(c) (i) Graphite is very unreactive [1] to most of the products of electrolysis.
(ii) Aluminium. [1]
(d) Tungsten has a very high melting point [1] and will sustain the white-hot conditions needed in a light bulb without melting.
(e) Copper carbonate decomposes [1] on heating to a different compound.
(f) Two of them: candle wax and sodium metal [1].

**Total: 8 marks**

***Question 5***

(a) $C_3H_8(g) \rightarrow C_3H_6(g) + H_2(g)$ [1]

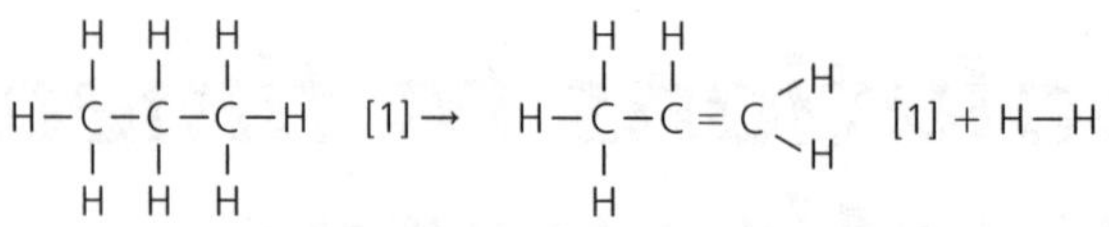

```
    H  H  H              H  H
    |  |  |              |  |   ,H
H - C -C - C - H  [1]→ H - C - C = C        [1] + H - H
    |  |  |              |      `H
    H  H  H              H
```

One mark for each structure as shown.

(b) (i) An addition reaction is a reaction in which more than one molecule joins together to form a single larger molecule. [1]

(ii)

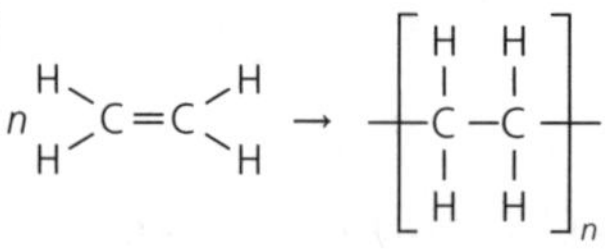

```
   H      H          [ H  H ]
n   >C=C<     →    --[-C - C-]--
   H      H          [ H  H ]n
```

Two marks for the correct structural equation – one mark for each side.

(c) Poly(propene) is used to make plastic chairs; parts for cars; agricultural 'string'; and carpets. [1]
(d) $C_3H_8(g) \rightarrow CH_4 + C_2H_4$
One mark for each correct product formula in a full equation.
(e) From the equation for the cracking of ethane it is seen that some bonds are broken and some are formed:

Bonds broken 2 × C–H plus 1 × C–C totalling 2 × 435 = 348 = 1218 kJ [1]
Bonds formed 1 × H–H plus 1 × C=C totalling −436 + −600 = −1036 kJ [1]
The difference is +182 kJ [1].

HINT
*Note that the signs of the energies for bond breaking are +, and those for bond formation are −.*

(f) 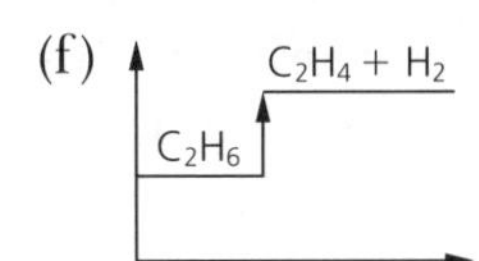


One mark for the upward direction of the energy level change.

(g) The figures are the same because the same bonds are broken [1] and formed [1] during both reactions.

**Total: 14 marks**

### *Question 6*

(a) (i) A burette. [1] (ii) It would be coloured, and therefore impure. [1]

(b) Crystals that contain 'water of crystallisation' such as these, would be dehydrated. Instead of drying they would decompose to the anhydrous salt. [1]

(c) (i) Number of moles $= \frac{\text{volume}}{1000}(\text{cm}^3) = \frac{50 \times 2}{1000} = 0.1$ [1]

(ii) $Na_2SO_4.10H_2O = (2 \times 23) + 32 + (4 \times 16) = 10 \times (2 + 16) = 322\,g$ [1]
The equation shows that the number of moles formed is equal to half the moles of sodium hydroxide used, i.e. 0.05 moles. Therefore the mass formed is $0.05 \times 322 = 16.1\,g$. [1]

(iii) From the equation of the reaction the moles of sulphuric acid is half the moles of sodium hydroxide, i.e. 0.05 moles [1].

$$\text{moles or acid} = \frac{\text{volume} \times \text{molarity}}{1000} = \frac{62.5 \times M}{1000} = 0.05 \text{ [1]}$$

$$\text{Hence, by rearranging, } M = \frac{1000 \times 0.05}{62.5} = 0.8\,\text{mol dm}^{-3} \text{ [1]}$$

(d) Crystals deposit from a saturated solution on cooling. Much of the solute remains dissolved in the saturate solution. [1]

(e) (i) Solubility changes with temperature.[1]

(ii) In part (c) (ii) it was given that 16.1 grams of the salt were produced. In the stem it stated that 3.30 grams of crystals were extracted. The difference is the mass remaining in the 32.80 grams of saturated solution. So the solubility is:

$16.1 - 3.30 = 12.8\,g$ in $32.8\,g$ of solution [1]

$\frac{12.8 \times 100\,g}{32.8}$ [1] is present in 100 g of saturated solution = 39.02 g/100 g [1].

(f) Sodium hydrogensulphate [1] $NaHSO_4$ [1]

(g) The magnesium oxide of magnesium hydroxide required is not soluble in water. [1]

**Total: 17 marks**

### *Question 4*

(a) (i) 41 [1] (ii) 4 [1] (iii) Germanium is in Group IV [1].

(iv) 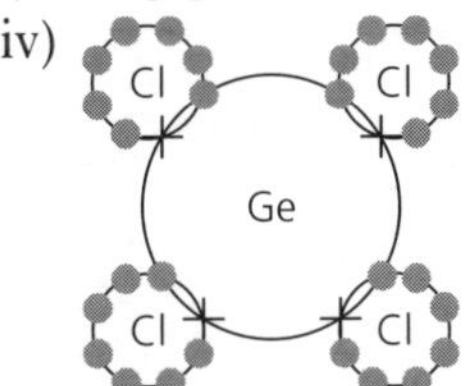


Eight electrons around Ge [1]; 8 electrons around at least one Cl [1]; but if you have drawn the formula as shown above then [3].

(b) (i) Amphoteric [1] because it is on the border region of metals and non-metals [1].

(ii) The high melting point suggest a giant structure [1] and the absence of conductivity indicates a molecular or covalent equivalent [1].
**Or** Giant covalent/giant molecular. [2]

(c) (i) $Ge_nH_{2n+2}$ [1]
(ii) $Ge_2H_6$ has a molecular mass of $2 \times 73 + 6 = 152$ [1].

The percentage of germanium is $\left(\frac{2 \times 73}{152}\right) \times 100$[1] = **96(.05)%** [1]

**Total: 14 marks**

### *Question 5*

(a) $Zn(s) + H_2SO_4\,(aq) \rightarrow ZnSO_4\,(aq) + H_2(g)$

One mark for three or more state symbols. One mark for the rest.

(b) Volume [1] of hydrogen [1] in $cm^3$ [1].

(c) The mass of zinc [1] could have doubled [1].

(d) Zinc reacts with copper sulphate displacing copper [1]. This uses up some of the zinc which reduces the volume of the hydrogen [1]. The copper acts as a catalyst for the reaction of zinc with the acid [1], so the graph slope is increased [1]. Any two of these answers for two marks.

(e) $Zn^{2+} + 2e^- \rightarrow Zn$ [1]

(f) (i) A solid mixture of metals is an alloy. [1]
(ii) Brass [1] is a mixture of zinc and copper.

(g) Zinc is more reactive than iron [1] and dissolves, producing electrons [1].

$Zn \rightarrow Zn^{2+} + 2e^-$ [1]

The electrons enter the iron metal and prevent the corrosion process [1] by preventing/reversing the corrosion reaction:

$Fe(s) \rightleftarrows Fe^{2+} + 2e^-$ [1]

Any three points for the maximum three marks.

**Total: 15 marks**

**Grading**

80% (64 marks) would gain a Grade A.

60% (48 marks) would gain a Grade B.

40% (32 marks) would gain a Grade C.

*part V*
# Data pages

## The Periodic Table of the Elements

| I | II | | | | | | Group | | | | | III | IV | V | VI | VII | 0 |
|---|---|---|---|---|---|---|---|---|---|---|---|---|---|---|---|---|---|
| | | | | | | | 1 H Hydrogen 1 | | | | | | | | | | 4 He Helium 2 |
| 7 Li Lithium 3 | 9 Be Beryllium 4 | | | | | | | | | | | 11 B Boron 5 | 12 C Carbon 6 | 14 N Nitrogen 7 | 16 O Oxygen 8 | 19 F Fluorine 9 | 20 Ne Neon 10 |
| 23 Na Sodium 11 | 24 Mg Magnesium 12 | | | | | | | | | | | 27 Al Aluminium 13 | 28 Si Silicon 14 | 31 P Phosphorus 15 | 32 S Sulphur 16 | 35.5 Cl Chlorine 17 | 40 Ar Argon 18 |
| 39 K Potassium 19 | 40 Ca Calcium 20 | 45 Sc Scandium 21 | 48 Ti Titanium 22 | 51 V Vanadium 23 | 52 Cr Chromium 24 | 55 Mn Manganese 25 | 56 Fe iron 26 | 59 Co Cobalt 27 | 59 Ni Nickel 28 | 64 Cu Copper 29 | 65 Zn Zinc 30 | 70 Ga Gallium 31 | 73 Ge Germanium 32 | 75 As Arsenic 33 | 79 Se Selenium 34 | 80 Br Bromine 35 | 84 Kr Krypton 36 |
| 85 Rb Rubidium 37 | 88 Sr Strontium 38 | 89 Y Yttrium 39 | 91 Zr Zirconium 40 | 93 Nb Niobium 41 | 96 Mo Molybdenum 42 | Tc Technetium 43 | 101 Ru Ruthenium 44 | 103 Rh Rhodium 45 | 106 Pd Palladium 46 | 108 Ag Silver 47 | 112 Cd Cadmium 48 | 115 In Indium 49 | 119 Sn Tin 50 | 122 Sb Antimony 51 | 128 Te Tellurium 52 | 127 I Iodine 53 | 131 Xe Xenon 54 |
| 133 Cs Caesium 55 | 137 Ba Barium 56 | 139 La Lanthanum 57 * | 178 Hf Hafnium 72 | 181 Ta Tantalum 73 | 184 W Tungsten 74 | 186 Re Rhenium 75 | 190 Os Osmium 76 | 192 Ir Indium 77 | 195 Pt Platinum 78 | 195 Au Gold 79 | 197 Hg Mercury 80 | 201 Tl Thallium 81 | 204 Pb Lead 82 | 207 Bi Bismuth 83 | 209 Po Polonium 84 | At Astatine 85 | Rn Radon 86 |
| Fr Francium 87 | 226 Ra Radium 88 | 227 Ac Actinium 89 t | | | | | | | | | | | | | | | |

* 58–71 Lanthanoid series
t 90–103 Actinoid series

| 140 Ce Cerium 58 | 141 Pr Praseodymium 59 | 144 Nd Neodymium 60 | Pm Promethium 61 | 150 Sm Samarium 62 | 152 Eu Europium 63 | 157 Gd Gadolinium 64 | 159 Tb Terbium 65 | 162 Dy Dysprosium 66 | 165 Ho Holmium 67 | 167 Er Erbium 68 | 169 Tm Thulium 69 | 173 Yb Ytterbium 70 | 175 Lu Lutetium 71 |
|---|---|---|---|---|---|---|---|---|---|---|---|---|---|
| 232 Th Thorium 90 | Pa Protactinium 91 | 238 U Uranium 92 | Np Neptunium 93 | Pu Plutonium 94 | Am Americium 95 | Cm Curium 96 | Bk Berkelium 97 | Cf Californium 98 | Es Einsteinium 99 | Fm Fermium 100 | Md Mendelevium 101 | No Nobelium 102 | Lr Lawrencium 103 |

Key: a X b — a relative atomic mass; X atomic symbol; b proton (atomic) number

The volume of one mole of any gas is 24 $dm^3$ at room temperature and pressure (r.t.p.)

## Formula of some common ions

| ***Positive ions*** | | ***Negative ions*** | |
|---|---|---|---|
| ***Name*** | ***Formula*** | ***Name*** | ***Formula*** |
| Aluminium | $Al^{3+}$ | Bromide | $Br^-$ |
| Ammonium | $NH_4^+$ | Carbonate | $CO_3^{2-}$ |
| Barium | $Ba^{2+}$ | Chloride | $Cl^-$ |
| Calcium | $Ca^{2+}$ | Fluoride | $F^-$ |
| Copper(II) | $Cu^{2+}$ | Hydroxide | $OH^-$ |
| Hydrogen | $H^+$ | Iodide | $I^-$ |
| Iron(II) | $Fe^{2+}$ | Nitrate | $NO_3^-$ |
| Iron(III) | $Fe^{3+}$ | Oxide | $O^{2-}$ |
| Lithium | $Li^+$ | Sulphate | $SO_4^{2-}$ |
| Magnesium | $Mg^{2+}$ | | |
| Nickel | $Ni^{2+}$ | | |
| Potassium | $K^+$ | | |
| Silver | $Ag^+$ | | |
| Sodium | $Na^+$ | | |

## Universal indicator

| ***pH*** | 4 | 5 | 6 | 7 | 8 | 9 | 10 |
|---|---|---|---|---|---|---|---|
| ***Colour*** | red | orange | yellow | green | blue | dark blue | violet |

You will note that these are the colours in the visible spectrum.

## Reactivity Series

*For metals*

Most reactive: Potassium
Sodium
Lithium
Calcium
Magnesium
Aluminium
(Carbon)
Zinc
Iron
(Hydrogen)
Tin
Lead
Copper
Silver
Least reactive: Gold

*For non-metals*

Most reactive: Fluorine
Chlorine
Oxygen
Bromine
Iodine
Least reactive: Sulphur

## Properties of gases

Remember the mnemonic **COWSLIPS**: **C**olour; **O**dour (smell); **W**eight (density); **S**olubility; **L**itmus; **I**nflammability; **P**oisonous; **S**upport burning.

*Coloured gas*

- **Chlorine** Green
- **Nitrogen dioxide** Brown
- **Hydrogen chloride** Colourless, fumes in moist air
- **Iodine** **Purple**

*Odour (smell)*

HINT
*All gases that smell are poisonous (see (a)) together with carbon monoxide.*

- **Chlorine** Pungent
- **Ammonia** Makes eyes water
- **Sulphur dioxide** Choking
- **Hydrogen chloride** Pungent, leaves a sour taste in the mouth

*Weight/density*

If a gas has a relative formula mass (RFM) greater than 30 it is denser than air; if it is less than 30, it is less dense than air. (The figures in brackets show the RFM.)

| *Denser* | *Less dense* |
|---|---|
| Chlorine (71) | Hydrogen (2) |
| Carbon dioxide (44) | Ammonia (17) |
| Hydrogen chloride (36.5) | Methane (16) |

*Solubility in water*

| *Soluble* | *Insoluble/slightly soluble* |
|---|---|
| Hydrogen chloride | Hydrogen |
| Ammonia | Carbon monoxide |
| Carbon dioxide | Oxygen |
| Chlorine | Nitrogen |

***Damp Litmus***

| *Acidic* | *Alkaline* |
|---|---|
| Hydrogen chloride | Ammonia |
| Sulphur dioxide | |
| Chlorine (then bleaches it) | |

***Flammability***

- **Hydrogen** burns with a 'pop'.
- **Carbon dioxide** burns with a blue flame.
- **Hydrocarbons** burn with a blue flame that gets more yellow and more smoky as the percentage of hydrogen in the hydrocarbon increases.
- **Oxygen** re-lights a glowing splint.

**LONGMAN HOMEWORK HANDBOOKS (KEY STAGE 3)**

*£7.99 each unless otherwise stated*

| | QTY *(0582)* | | |
|---|---|---|---|
| 1 | _____ | 29330 8 | English (KS3) |
| 2 | _____ | 29331 6 | French (KS3) |
| 3 | _____ | 30423 7 | French pack*(KS3) (£12.99) |
| 4 | _____ | 30425 3 | French cassette (KS3) (£6.00) |
| 5 | _____ | 29329 4 | German (KS3) |
| 6 | _____ | 30427 X | German pack*(KS3) (£12.99) |
| 7 | _____ | 30428 8 | German cassette (KS3) (£6.00) |
| 8 | _____ | 29328 6 | Mathematics (KS3) |
| 9 | _____ | 29327 8 | Science (KS3) |

**LONGMAN GCSE STUDY GUIDES**

*£9.99 each unless otherwise stated*

| | | | |
|---|---|---|---|
| 10 | _____ | 30481 4 | Biology |
| 11 | _____ | 31538 7 | Business Studies |
| 12 | _____ | 30482 2 | Chemistry |
| 13 | _____ | 31302 3 | Design and Technology |
| 14 | _____ | 31539 5 | Economics |
| 15 | _____ | 30484 9 | English |
| 16 | _____ | 30483 0 | English Literature |
| 17 | _____ | 30485 7 | French |
| 18 | _____ | 32018 6 | French pack* (£14.99) |
| 19 | _____ | 32019 4 | French cassette (£6.00) |
| 20 | _____ | 30486 5 | Geography |
| 21 | _____ | 30487 3 | German |
| 22 | _____ | 32020 8 | German pack* (£14.99) |
| 23 | _____ | 32021 6 | German cassette (£6.00) |
| 24 | _____ | 30495 4 | Higher Level Mathematics |
| 25 | _____ | 30494 6 | Information Technology (£10.99) |
| 26 | _____ | 30496 2 | Mathematics |
| 27 | _____ | 30497 0 | Music |
| 28 | _____ | 31540 9 | Physics |
| 29 | _____ | 28700 6 | Psychology |
| 30 | _____ | 31542 5 | Religious Studies |
| 31 | _____ | 30498 9 | Science (£10.99) |
| 32 | _____ | 22651 1 | Sociology |
| 33 | _____ | 30499 7 | Spanish |
| 34 | _____ | 24509 5 | Spanish pack* (£14.99) |
| 35 | _____ | 24511 7 | Spanish cassette (£6.00) |
| 36 | _____ | 30545 4 | World History |

**LONGMAN GCSE EXAM PRACTICE KITS**

| | | | |
|---|---|---|---|
| 37 | _____ | 30381 8 | Biology (£4.99) |
| 38 | _____ | 30383 4 | Business Studies (£4.99) |
| 39 | _____ | 31190 X | Chemistry (£4.99) |
| 40 | _____ | 31191 8 | English (£4.99) |
| 41 | _____ | 31253 1 | French (£4.99) |
| 42 | _____ | 31252 3 | German (£4.99) |
| 43 | _____ | 30384 2 | Geography (£4.99) |
| 44 | _____ | 31251 5 | Higher Mathematics (£4.99) |
| 45 | _____ | 31249 3 | Information Technology (£4.99) |
| 46 | _____ | 30385 0 | Mathematics (£4.99) |
| 47 | _____ | 30379 6 | Physics (£4.99) |
| 48 | _____ | 30380 X | Science (£5.99) |

**GCSE SURVIVAL GUIDE** *£2.95*

49 _____ 05078 2

_____ **YORK NOTES LITERATURE GUIDES** *(see overleaf)*

**LONGMAN A-LEVEL STUDY GUIDES**

*£9.99 each unless otherwise stated*

| | | | |
|---|---|---|---|
| 50 | _____ | 22569 8 | Accounting (£10.99) |
| 51 | _____ | 31545 X | Biology |
| 52 | _____ | 31652 9 | Business Studies |
| 53 | _____ | 31546 8 | Chemistry |
| 54 | _____ | 05782 5 | Computer Science |
| 55 | _____ | 27688 8 | Economics (£10.99) |
| 56 | _____ | 31656 1 | English |
| 57 | _____ | 05784 1 | French |
| 58 | _____ | 24495 1 | French pack* (£14.99) |
| 59 | _____ | 24497 8 | French cassette (£6.00) |
| 60 | _____ | 05173 8 | Geography |
| 61 | _____ | 31654 5 | German |
| 62 | _____ | 24498 6 | German pack* (£14.99) |
| 63 | _____ | 24508 7 | German cassette (£6.00) |
| 64 | _____ | 28702 2 | Government and Politics (£10.99) |
| 65 | _____ | 31549 2 | Law (£10.99) |
| 66 | _____ | 31550 6 | Mathematics (£10.99) |
| 67 | _____ | 31551 4 | Modern History |
| 68 | _____ | 27690 X | Physics |
| 69 | _____ | 31655 3 | Psychology |
| 70 | _____ | 27691 8 | Sociology |

**LONGMAN A-LEVEL EXAM PRACTICE KITS** *£6.99 each*

| | | | |
|---|---|---|---|
| 71 | _____ | 30386 9 | Biology |
| 72 | _____ | 31245 0 | British and European Modern History |
| 73 | _____ | 30387 7 | Business Studies |
| 74 | _____ | 30388 5 | Chemistry |
| 75 | _____ | 31250 7 | Economics |
| 76 | _____ | 31248 5 | French |
| 77 | _____ | 31254 X | Geography |
| 78 | _____ | 31247 7 | German |
| 79 | _____ | 30389 3 | Mathematics |
| 80 | _____ | 31243 4 | Physics |
| 81 | _____ | 30390 7 | Psychology |
| 82 | _____ | 30382 6 | Sociology |

**LONGMAN PARENT'S AND STUDENTS' GUIDES**

*£2.99 each*

| | | | |
|---|---|---|---|
| 83 | _____ | 29971 3 | Longman Parent's Guide to Pre-school Choices and Nursery Education |
| 84 | _____ | 29975 6 | Longman Parent's Guide to Key Stage 1 of the National Curriculum |
| 85 | _____ | 29974 8 | Longman Parent's Guide to Key Stage 2 of the National Curriculum |
| 86 | _____ | 29973 X | Longman Parent's Guide to Key Stage 3 of the National Curriculum |
| 87 | _____ | 29972 1 | Longman Parent's Guide to GCSE and Key Stage 4 of the National Curriculum |
| 88 | _____ | 29978 0 | Longman A-level Survival Guide |
| 89 | _____ | 29969 1 | Longman Students' Guide to Vocational Education |
| 90 | _____ | 29970 5 | Longman Students' Guide to Returning to Learning |
| 91 | _____ | 29976 4 | Longman Students' Guide to Higher Education |

** pack = book and cassette*

## Get Revising — *Weeks 9 to 4*

Working on the basis of covering two topics per week an ideal pattern to follow for each week would be:

Read through your class notes and coursework.

Summarise the main points:

- write down the main principles/theories
- outline key terms and definitions
- note important examples/illustrations
- list important data/formula

(Using a highlighter pen is very useful here)

Practise answering exam questions:

- work through the questions in your Longman Exam Practice Kits
- write outline answers
- write full answers to some questions giving yourself the same time as in the exam
- make sure that you try to answer questions of each type set in the exam
- check your answers with those provided in your Longman Exam Practice Kit. Learn from any mistakes you have made.

## Get Confidence — *Weeks 3 to 1*

- ➤ Have a final read through of all your class notes and coursework.
- ➤ Read through the summaries you have already made.
- ➤ Try to reduce these summary notes to a single side of A4 paper.
- ➤ Test yourself to check that you can remember everything on each A4 page.
- ➤ Go over the practice questions already attempted.

*The day before the exams*

- ➤ Read through each A4 summary sheet.
- ➤ Check that you have all the equipment you need for the exam.
- ➤ Do something you enjoy in the evening.
- ➤ Go to bed reasonably early: tired students rarely give their best.

*The exam – get up and go*

- ➤ Have a good breakfast to give you energy.
- ➤ Don't panic – everyone else is nervous too.
- ➤ Remember – the examiners are looking for opportunities to give you marks, not take them away!

***Good luck!***

| No. of weeks before the exams | Date: Week commencing | MONDAY | TUESDAY | WEDNESDAY | THURSDAY | FRIDAY | SATURDAY | SUNDAY |
|---|---|---|---|---|---|---|---|---|
| 9 | | | | | | | | |
| 8 | | | | | | | | |
| 7 | | | | | | | | |
| 6 | | | | | | | | |
| 5 | | | | | | | | |
| 4 | | | | | | | | |
| 3 | | | | | | | | |
| 2 | | | | | | | | |
| 1 | | | | | | | | |

# LONGMAN EXAM PRACTICE KITS

# REVISION PLANNER

Titles Available –

**GCSE**
Biology
Business Studies
Chemistry
English
French
Geography
German
Higher Maths
Information Systems
Mathematics
Physics
Science

**A-LEVEL**
Biology
British and European Modern History
Business Studies
Chemistry
Economics
French
Geography
German
Mathematics
Physics
Psychology
Sociology

There are lots of ways to revise. It is important to find what works best for you. Here are some suggestions:

- try testing with a friend: testing each other can be fun!
- label or highlight sections of text and make a checklist of these items.
- learn to write summaries – these will be useful for revision later.
- try reading out loud to yourself.
- don't overdo it – the most effective continuous revision session is probably between forty and sixty minutes long.
- practise answering past exam papers and test yourself using the same amount of time as you will have on the actual day – this will help to make the exam itself less daunting.
- pace yourself, taking it step by step.

**Getting Started** *Begin on week 12*

Use a calendar to put dates onto your planner and write in the dates of your exams. Fill in your targets for each day. Be realistic when setting the targets, and try your best to stick to them. If you miss a revision period, remember to re-schedule it for another time.

**Get Familiar** *Weeks 12 and 11*

Identify the topics on your syllabuses. Get to know the format of the papers – time, number of questions, types of questions. Start reading through your class notes, coursework, etc.

**Get Serious** *Week 10*

Complete reading through your notes – you should now have an overview of the whole syllabus. Choose 12 topics to study in greater depth for each subject. Allocate two topic areas for each subject for each of the next 6 weeks

| No. of weeks before the exams | Date: Week commencing | MONDAY | TUESDAY | WEDNESDAY | THURSDAY | FRIDAY | SATURDAY | SUNDAY |
|---|---|---|---|---|---|---|---|---|
| 12 | | | | | | | | |
| 11 | | | | | | | | |
| 10 | | | | | | | | |